The Apple of My Eye

Trusting God's Guidance When We Can't See

AMY BETH PEDERSON

Amy's exquisitely observed *The Apple of My Eye* is an offering of keen insight, nuanced writing, and unforgettable story of walking out life with the one you love in the face of an incredibly rare medical diagnosis. Amy's writing weaves complex pathos in and through the day-to-day practicalities required to keep going when the unthinkable happens as it did with her husband. The reader facing an equally daunting situation will find solace in her insights and appreciate the directness by which she tells her story.

JULIE BARNHILL

Author

Speaker

What a gift Amy has given us in *The Apple of My Eye*. Learning the hard way what it truly means to love your spouse in sickness and in health, she walked the heartbreaking journey with her husband, Seth, who was diagnosed with ocular melanoma and eventually went to his heavenly home. Although it was hard as a loving caregiver and mother of three children, she was like Jesus to him as she humbly cared for Seth, always fighting by his side for a cure.

Surrendering her will and trusting that this was all part of God's plan, she was able to rest in this role even though she would never have chosen it for herself.

Together this young family experienced holy moments where God met them in their pain. And although Amy admits that her personality is introspective, God brought a loving community of friends and family to walk the journey with them, sharing in both the laughter and tears.

Instead of living in sorrow and letting her pain be wasted, Amy chose God in her darkest hour and is now sharing her story to bring glory to Him.

BEV DESALVO

Author of Return to Joy
Widow of Gary DeSalvo Who Died from Ocular Melanoma in 2019

The Apple of My Eye will open your eyes to the struggle, the "behind the scenes," and the ever- present hope you find while walking a loved one through cancer. Amy did a beautiful job of combining honesty, vulnerability, and faith as she shared her journey of walking her husband home.

TARA DICKSON

Writer at www.taradickson.com
Podcaster at Seek and Savor
Widow Mama

In these pages Amy has given us an up-close look at an impossible journey. Here, she threads the space between sharing about the painful reality of walking with a loved one through cancer, while holding a steady line of hope out to readers. Encouraging, kind, and thoughtful, this book is a tender companion for those facing their own journey through cancer.

KRIS CAMEALY

Author of Everything Is Yours: How Giving God Your Whole Heart
Changes Your Whole Life
Founder & Director of Refine {the retreat}
Writer at www.kriscamealy.com

"If I had written our story, I wouldn't have written it this way," writes Amy. "This is not normal." To enter these pages is to join Amy and her husband in a sacred journey on an unplanned path with a "misbehaving tumor" combined with mission trips, a job change, and a major cross-country move. This is a book for caregivers, for potential caregivers, and for those who care for caregivers. It's a book for those who face the unexpected and the uncertain. It's a book for those who need the tiniest key to hope. It's a call to live "every single blessed day" with no regrets.

SANDRA HESKA KING, RN, BSN

Writer at www.sandraheskaking.com
Writer as part of the Compassion International Sponsor Trip 2015

Amy Pederson's *The Apple of My Eye* is a must read for cancer caregivers. Amy's emotional authenticity allows us to not just read her words, but to feel her journey in our hearts. Her storytelling will bring comfort, validation, and a reminder that there is "beauty in the midst of significant pain."

MADDIE RITTER, LICSW

Program Manager and Clinical Social Worker at Cancer Pathways

In this surprising book, Amy beautifully combines memoir, reflection, artistry, pain, honor, and honesty. Page after rapidly turning page, she weaves it all together, bringing us with her as she adroitly handles the deeply personal aspects of love of husband, God, family, and daily life, spoken through dozens of nuanced, delightful conversations and observations. She skillfully utilizes the most difficult alongside the simplest moments, all bringing meaning. Her stated goal is to bring pure beauty in the midst of significant pain. She nails it. This book will move you, delight you, sadden you, cause you to reflect, and bring you hope and joy. Very highly recommended!

KEITH ROBINSON

Pastor of Riverwood Covenant Church, MN

The day the doctors tell you that you have an aggressive cancer with no known cure is the day you fully understand how fragile and temporal your life becomes. In this book, Amy eloquently and succinctly captures the chaos that follows – in your marriage, your faith, your hope. Suddenly you are living Psalms 23; walking through the valley of the shadow of death is no longer an abstract or poetic psalm but becomes your new reality. Bloody knees and bent over trees. Amy captures the journey with refreshing candor and humility, and yet the book is an easy read; inspirational and instructive.

PETER ILLYN

Metastatic Uveal Melanoma Warrior

The Apple of My Eye is a beautiful love story. It is a story of faith, hope in its purest form, and love at its deepest level. Amy, a master storyteller, shares the five-year journey she and Seth took together while holding hands, trusting God to guide them on the crooked, rocky, narrow paths they could not see. Together they openly and lovingly shared the journey nobody ever wants to take with their children, parents, and extended family, and now with us. Amy and Seth's beautiful wedding vows were tested when the promise to love "in sickness and health" became urgent, raw, and real in the face of Seth's cancer diagnosis. This love story is one of hard-fought battles, tenacity, research, uncharted trails and trials, no stone unturned, no paths unexplored, and no regrets. This is a love story of endless hope and deep abiding faith intermingled with positive, joyful attitudes, upbeat music, laughter through tears, questions, and sweet surrender of all things into God's amazing love and care. This is a love story and a journey you don't want to miss. It's a love story full to overflowing with joy lived out from deep within, a knowing of God's amazing grace, and of the blessed hope for tomorrow.

ANNA EVANS

Retired Teacher
Storyteller
hope*writer

If you are a caregiver or know someone battling for their health, this book is for you. Amy invites you as a close friend to walk alongside her as she navigates the news of her husband's rare cancer diagnosis and the fight of her own to support him emotionally, physically, and spiritually, all while raising children and navigating treatment options and the healthcare system. Inspiring and enlightening, Amy's experience chronicles moments when God uses others to encourage and strengthen their family on the journey. Her testimony offers us a look at living with hope in the midst of uncertainty and how to be a strong, humble, loving, and relentless advocate as wife and mother. Amy and Seth fought cancer valiantly and their story demonstrates how God's grace and love are evident even in our darkest trials.

KATIE MALLORY, M.A.

Wife and Mother of Three
Daughter of Mom Who Battled Cancer and is now with Jesus
Former Account Executive at World Vision

Amy's heart is immediately revealed and her fierce determination is duly noted. Her loyalty to the raw and organic journey as caregiver through her husband's cancer will evoke an awakening in your heart that will leave you changed. Amy intricately pens and uncovers a story of epic love that is both tragic and triumphant. You will be stirred deeply by her eloquence and the desire for her reader to bear witness to the significance of her own story. Her words are clothed in majestic grace and unshakable faith. Be prepared to feel ALL THE FEELS with this gift.

MONICA PALMER

Wife and Mama
Seeker of Grace and Truth
Lover of Coffee and All Things Chocolate

The Apple of My Eye

Trusting God's Guidance When We Can't See

AMY BETH PEDERSON

your story studio

your story studio

The Apple of My Eye: Trusting God's Guidance When We Can't See

Copyright © 2020 by Amy Beth Pederson

Library of Congress Cataloging-in-Publication Data

Names: Pederson, Amy Beth, author.

Title: The apple of my eye : trusting God's guidance when we can't see / Amy Beth Pederson.

Description: Includes bibliographical references. | North Bend, WA: Your Story Studio, 2020.

Identifiers: LCCN: 2020909077 | ISBN: 978-0-9999018-1-6 (pbk.) | 978-0-9999018-2-3 (ebook)

Subjects: LCSH Pederson, Amy Beth. | Pederson, Amy Beth—Family. | Cancer—Patients—Family relationships—United States. | Husband and wife. | Bereavement—Religious aspects—Christianity. | Grief—Religious aspects—Christianity. | Loss (Psychology)— Religious aspects—Christianity. | BISAC BIOGRAPHY & AUTOBIOGRAPHY / Personal Memoirs | HEALTH & FITNESS / Diseases / Cancer | RELIGION / Christian Living / Death, Grief, Bereavement

Classification: LCC BV4908 .P43 2020 | DDC 248.8/6/092--dc2

Cover Design: Taryn Nergaard, Typewriter Creative Co.
Cover Photography: Stefanie Amm/EyeEm, Adobe Stock
Imprint Logo Design: Lilac + Love Designs
Interior Design and Typeset: Taryn Nergaard, Typewriter Creative Co.
Editing: Jennie Scott, Typewriter Creative Co.
Author Photography: Claire Meyer Photography

Published by Your Story Studio, North Bend, Washington 98045

First Edition 2020 / Printed in the United States of America

*For Cooper, Elsa and Maisie,
so you know we tried everything.*

CONTENTS

FOREWORD

I met Amy and her husband, Seth, in 2015 when I hit the road for a season of playing summer festivals as I toured a new album. My team and I had decided a great way to connect the dots of all the stops in random places was to play some house shows on our route. Having no experience with house shows, I didn't know what to expect. I didn't know what it would be like hanging out in the living rooms of people I'd just met. I certainly never expected to form lasting friendships. But so it was with the Pedersons.

I remember how warm, friendly, and fun the family was from the moment we pulled into their driveway. How cozy it felt when all the chairs full of people were packed into their living room. How we ate pizza in the kitchen together after the show was over, and how Seth dropped a carton of milk from the fridge all over the floor while trying to pack in the snacks left over from the evening. I even remember meeting some of their extended family the next day, and so enjoying the warmth and kindness of this Midwestern clan.

At some point during our time together, the topic of eyes came up. I can't remember exactly why, but since I cannot see, it usually does arise at some point. Seth casually mentioned that his vision had been impaired for a moment in time during treatment for eye cancer, but it was expressed as no big deal, something in the past. Even then, I marveled at the calm, inner courage I could see he and Amy possessed.

The Pedersons and I would continue to meet up a few other times for house shows and hang time when I was in the Minneapolis area. Through these meetings, I was introduced to Amy's beautiful and insightful writings. I found her descriptions of everyday life so captivating because of their candor, a trait that is infused in this book.

I remember well our last adventure together. We went to pick up a new lens for Amy's camera as she told me of her budding excitement about professional photography. Seth was in a season of searching for a new job, which ultimately ended in a move all the way across the country to Seattle. After their move to the West Coast, we only occasionally corresponded via text, but I thought of the Pedersons often and prayed they were enjoying their new surroundings and adventures.

When Amy let me know that Seth's cancer had returned, I was stunned. Even more so when I learned the end was near. I was constantly moved to tears as I read Amy's compelling life chronicles over several years. Her writing exuded courage and grace in the midst of pain and confusion. She has a way of finding threads of hope in the otherwise bleak and hopeless. And this is why I am so thankful that so many readers will get to experience firsthand this powerful telling of her story.

The Apple of My Eye is as joyful and inspiring as it is painful and heart-wrenching. It poses questions that don't have clear answers, except that there is always hope. Not fluffy optimism-type hope, but rich hope that only a deep faith in God and His purposes can bring. I encourage you to consider what it means to have such hope as the Pedersons' story unfolds before you.

GINNY OWENS

Singer
Songwriter
Speaker

Rejoice always,
pray continually,
give thanks in all circumstances;
for this is God's will for you in Christ Jesus.

— 1 Thessalonians 5:16-18

INTRODUCTION

I believed in the power of writing things down way back to July 4, 1988. I was 12 years old and had just cracked open my first diary – hot pink with an ice cream cone on top - to begin documenting my days. One diary turned into two, then three. Diaries turned into notebooks, and notebooks turned into journals – teenage drama journals, gratitude journals, love journals, first job journals, pregnancy journals, and first-time mom journals.

But shortly after the birth of our first child, there was a shifting. In the spring of 2003, God planted a seed in me to become a published author.

Between 2004 and 2010, I kept a private journal about my sister's battles with addiction and mental health and how that journey impacted me as her sister. In 2012, I launched a website where I publish stories about the divine in the daily, loving what you live and living what you love, about seeing the significance of your story and honoring it as true. Between 2016 and 2017, I spent much of my writing energy composing frequent Facebook and Caring Bridge updates as our family accompanied my dad through a rare lung disease, lung transplant, and recovery.

Yes, God certainly planted seeds for me to become a published author. In fact, I was so sure He was calling me that I left my near 15-year career in late December 2014 to pursue writing and professional photography.

But just three weeks after I left my career as a speech-language pathologist to pursue writing and photography, we received the news that my husband had cancer, a rare form of eye cancer called choroidal melanoma. I turned to writing, once again, to process my thoughts and feelings, to share medical updates with loved ones, and to birth something beautiful out of the tragedy that had befallen our family. I remained faithful throughout the cancer journey, writing and publishing posts on my website for five years and two months between 2015 and 2020. I had no intentions of those writings becoming a book, but when I published the last post after my husband's passing, I realized those writings WERE a book.

So here we are.

God planted the seeds, and 17 years later, I am seeing the first fruits.

The Apple of My Eye is our cancer story from the day of diagnosis to the day of passing and much of what was in between. It's the compilation of posts I published on my website between 2015 and 2020, plus bonus content to fill gaps in the story. It isn't perfect. It isn't comprehensive by any means (I'll save the rest of the story for another book.) But it's true.

There's a reason the journey led us here, to this place, this time, this moment in my story and yours. Cancer or no cancer, you are hereby invited to witness the mystery of my life intersecting uniquely with yours. May you turn each page, trusting the Spirit will stir you to see something new. May you discover something that surprises you. May you dare to live greatly, serve well, and see the beauty in hard, uncertain things. May my words edify your soul. May you know in the deepest, most tender places of your heart that God is guiding you even when you can't see a single way through whatever it is you're facing. May you gather bits and pieces, perhaps even bushels and baskets full of wisdom for the journey ahead. Blessed be this story, my story, your story, our story. Praise the God who was, and is, and is to come.

1

THE APPLE OF MY EYE

January 26, 2015

Less than 48 hours before I was scheduled to leave for my trip to the Dominican Republic with Compassion International, my husband, Seth, called to share the news that he had choroidal melanoma, a rare form of eye cancer affecting 6 in 1 million people. I'd just finished my morning workout when he called and had a whole day of packing and preparing planned for the day ahead. But as I talked to my husband at the entrance to the gym, I began to feel sick. Literally sick. Packing and preparing for my upcoming trip was urgent, yes. But this was life altering and needed my attention today.

The day before, Seth had gone in for a routine eye appointment. He shared with the optometrist that he'd been experiencing constant but dim strobing lights in the corner of his right eye. She evaluated further, told him he likely had a detached retina, and made him an appointment with an ophthalmologist the following morning at 8:00 a.m. We were told he'd need surgery to repair the detached retina that afternoon, so I was ready for anything the way it was. Little did we know, it wasn't a detached retina. It was eye cancer.

Seth didn't go into work that day. And I didn't pack or prepare for my trip as planned. We spent time together. We processed together. We ate lunch together. We called our parents together. We made a few key contacts together. We rested together. And in the evening, we shared the news with the kids together.

By the time Friday came rolling along, I was in full panic mode. I now had one day to do what I'd originally planned to do in two days. Not only that, I was battling confusion and emotion related to the fact that I was about to leave on the trip of a lifetime writing on behalf of Compassion International, while also facing the reality of my husband's cancer.

Immediately following Seth's diagnosis, the ophthalmologist contacted Mayo Clinic in Rochester, Minnesota, to see if Seth could be scheduled with one of the nation's leading doctors in the treatment of eye cancer. The doctor hadn't been taking new patients, but they wanted to see if there was any way Seth could get in with him. Fortunately, we got in. Well, we got penciled in for January 29-30. Our appointments weren't confirmed, but likely.

My husband and I agreed. While this was absolutely NOT an ideal scenario, there was NO reason for me to cancel my travel plans. The appointments had been penciled in at Mayo. In the meantime, there was nothing we could do but wait, so we decided to proceed as planned. I would go on the trip with Compassion International and live my dream of writing on behalf of children living in extreme poverty.

So yes, back to that Friday when I was packing and preparing like a maniac. I was non-stop all day long. In fact, it wasn't until 9:00 p.m. that I finally finished everything and tucked myself into bed. Unfortunately, I'd packed, prepared, and worked myself into a frenzy so much so that I didn't get a minute of sleep that night before the trip.

Seth and I refused to let this diagnosis get the best of us. I wanted that to hold true for my trip to the Dominican Republic with Compassion International, too. So Saturday morning, with zero minutes of sleep in me and a big trip ahead of me, I said good-bye to Seth in the dark of 2:45 a.m. and left to meet family friends who had graciously agreed to drive me to the airport. Later that afternoon in the Miami International Airport, I published a post explaining the state of my heart and soul at the start of this trip that meant the world to me. It was vague, but as specific as I could be without revealing my husband's recent eye cancer diagnosis. My goal was to embrace the trip wholeheartedly. I was bound and determined to keep it free of cancer talk.

The trip was amazing and an honor of a lifetime. I'd do it all over again in a heartbeat. But I shouldn't have been surprised when I experienced another near sleepless night midway through the trip and wasn't able to get the day's blog post published. I'd come to the end of myself. I was basically a wreck for the first part of a day. I was on this trip to give, yes. But I also needed to learn how to receive. Planning, preparing and executing had been close companions, but now I needed to surrender it all. God was already at work transforming me through my husband's eye cancer and the trip of my dreams.

It's been 10 days since I returned from my trip with Compassion International. We've already been to Mayo Clinic for three nights and 2 ½ days of appointments with doctors. I've spent most of my days in a foggy, exhausted state. My emotions have been all over the place. Neutral, angry, sad, distant, distracted, empty, and now finally back to normal for the most part.

We debated extensively about how to share medical updates with family and friends. A Caring Bridge site was recommended, but we decided it wasn't a fit for us. Seth considered starting a blog to document the journey. He even brainstormed titles, had a vision for his posts, and researched available URLs. But he decided the commitment to maintain a blog while managing his health and work would be too difficult. That left us with my website. While I never intended for my site to be a place to update family and friends about our life, it is a public place where people can pop in and read as they wish.

We agreed my website would be the best place to share our journey, but I still needed time to discern. I pondered in silence through days of exhaustion and uncertainty. I journaled on the days I wanted to write but wasn't in any mood to type or edit. I contemplated a scenario in which I'd remain completely silent about Seth's eye cancer on my website, but realized quickly that a silent approach isn't in line with who I am as a writer and would ultimately feel disingenuous to my readers.

Last week when we were at Mayo Clinic for three days, we finally decided to make the news public on Facebook. When more than 200 people responded with words of encouragement and promises of prayer, I knew right then and there that we had to find a way to update the caring circle of family and friends around us. Practically speaking, I'm in no emotional state to field non-stop calls, texts, and emails. The answer became clear from all angles – website it will be.

I'm approaching this journey gently, with as few expectations as possible. Because the truth is, we have no idea what to expect along the way. I'll write when I want to write, when I need to write, and when I'm able to write. I'll include factual updates, but won't use jargon you'd have to look up in a medical dictionary to understand. I'll incorporate insights, but won't reveal every detail of my private life as wife and caregiver. I'll tell stories and make observations about the world of cancer and medicine, caregiving and loving, believing and trusting in God's goodness, even when life throws you major curveballs. And yes, there will be references to patients and doctors, spouses and families, visitors and helpers along the way. Because we're all on this journey of life together. We're all here to learn from one another and love one another, even when life's hard.

So join us, will you?

He's positive. He's upbeat. He expects to get through this

without a hitch. He's approaching this with bravery, courage, and hope for the best possible outcomes. He's not looking for pity, sadness, or despair. Plentiful words of affirmation will suffice just fine for my man. Yes, he has eye cancer. But he's still the apple of my eye.

2

ACCLIMATING TO THE MEDICAL WORLD

January 27, 2015

I arrived back home from my trip to the Dominican Republic on Thursday night. On Friday morning, Seth received a phone call from Mayo Clinic notifying us that we needed to be there for two days of appointments for further evaluation of his eye cancer starting at 8:00 Tuesday morning.

There wasn't much time to prepare, so we quickly arranged child care for our two oldest and decided to bring our three-year-old "baby" with us. Because of the timing of the first appointment, we knew we'd need to travel to Mayo the night prior. I got right on the task of reserving two nights in a hotel, spending two hours scouring the internet for an affordable room that had decent customer ratings and was also a reasonable distance from Mayo Clinic.

It didn't take long for financial worries to set in regarding this journey on which we were embarking. **Two nights of hotel.** *Cha ching.* **Meals for three people for two days.**

Cha ching. **Gas two and from.** *Cha ching.* **Parking.** *Cha ching.* **Deductible, then 20% coinsurance for two days of appointments at Mayo Clinic.** *Cha ching.* Even with financial implications looming large, there's nothing we can do about it. The costs are a necessary part of restoring health. So we press on, knowing that medical bills will be the least of our worries if we can pull through the other side of this health crisis.

Tuesday morning came before we knew it. There we were in the hotel's breakfast nook eating scrambled eggs, sausage, and French toast. I noted a heaviness in the air the moment we walked in. It was a Tuesday morning, and most, if not all, the people in the room were there because of significant medical concerns.

Our three-year-old coughed while she was eating breakfast. I held a large, white napkin up to her mouth as quickly as I could and whispered to Seth, "We need to cover her mouth when she coughs in here. We need to be as careful as we can." Moments later, I got up to get more orange juice and overheard a lady speaking quietly to the breakfast attendant. "We just can't afford to take a chance. I'm here for eight weeks of chemo the way it is." It was then that I noticed the woman and her husband had moved tables AWAY from us, to the back corner of the room. Yep. I was right on those coughing concerns.

We knew we were getting close to Mayo when we started seeing an unusually large number of hotels and passed the "Limb Lab," the biggest and most beautiful store we'd ever seen dedicated to prosthetic limbs.

Mayo Clinic was on our right as we pulled in, and the parking garage was to the left. When we got out of the vehicle, our three-year-old said, "Is this where you work, daddy?" Seth replied, "No, this is where they're gonna make my eye better." She probed with another question, and Seth tenderly tried to pull the wool over her three-year-old eyes by responding with a vague, not-really-true answer. I noted to him quietly that it would probably be appropriate to share that his eye has an "owie" and the doctors are going to help him fix it. There was no reason to beat around the bush. Eventually, she was going to realize daddy has an "owie" on his eye, so we might as well begin addressing it now. Seth agreed, and all was well.

We proceeded to patient check-in, which was more like a gigantic hotel than a medical clinic. Seth received a detailed schedule for the next two days, but we were reminded that the schedule is subject to change at any moment. That first day, he was booked in back-to-back appointments from 8:00 a.m. to 12:30 p.m., including multiple vision exams, special photography and imaging of the eye, and blood work.

We made our way back to the area where Seth had most of his appointments. Seth was greeted warmly and called back immediately. I stayed in the waiting area with our three-year-old, trying to keep her quiet and entertained. Several individuals with thick eye patches came through as we waited. I couldn't help but believe this was a glimpse into our future.

After we'd been there a while, an elderly gentleman came over, sat down beside us, and gave our daughter a small bouncy ball. To be honest, I thought he was a little crazy. Give a three-year-old a bouncy ball in a waiting room at Mayo Clinic? Disaster in waiting. But it was great. Our daughter threw the ball much more gently than I would've ever guessed, and the scene brought smiles to people waiting near us and with us. I was wrong, so wrong. There was power in that bouncy ball, and there was power in the presence of my three-year-old playing innocently amidst such medical struggle. The fragility of the elderly woman seated in a wheelchair next to us struck me. She smiled ever so slightly when our daughter threw the ball. I wondered how much she could see. I wondered when the last time was that she was able to throw a ball, catch a ball, bend over to pick up a ball.

After two to three hours of waiting, our daughter wasn't tolerating waiting anymore, so we went out to the long hallway to change things up. I sat on a couch and made my sleepy self comfortable. Our daughter walked the window ledge. The dichotomy between her innocence and the medical world was evident once again. There she was walking the ledge as people talked about catheterizing, chemotherapy, "this is all we can do," and "I'm hanging in there. I'm tough you know." I pondered all the things our daughter doesn't know about yet. I pondered our perceived strength vs. real-life weaknesses. We're all walking on the ledge, really. We're all hanging in there as best as we can. We're all making the best out of situations that are less than ideal, whether this month's reality is chemotherapy or living paycheck to paycheck.

I finally gave up. Our daughter had been walking the ledge for who knows how long and I was getting sleepy sitting there on that couch. The exhaustion was really starting to set in from my trip to the Dominican Republic, four days acclimating to home, and now the trip to Mayo for Seth's eye cancer appointments. I'm pretty sure I fell asleep while our daughter watched silly surprise egg videos on YouTube. Just as I dozed off, Seth approached. He was done, but needed to head down to blood work. Off we went.

Blood work was crazy busy. Chairs and couches were lined in rows. I invited our daughter to pick a seat, and she invited daddy to sit down next to her. They enjoyed a few minutes together before he was called back.

All in all, Seth spent 4 1/2 hours in appointments that first day at Mayo. We ate lunch, took a nap in the hotel room, made best efforts to bring our daughter swimming, and joined Seth's cousin for dinner.

As we got ready for bed at the end of the day, I told Seth, "I can't quite seem to get my bearings. I feel like I'm totally out of routine." "You'd better get used to it," he said. "We're going to be out of routine for a while now."

Yep. Out of routine, we most definitely were. Out of routine, we most definitely are.

I brushed my teeth three times that first day. The familiarity and predictability of the habit I'd had since toddlerhood was oddly refreshing to my spirit in the midst of the unknown medical world to which we were quickly acclimating.

3

THE MELODY OF LIVING
AMIDST THE DYING

January 29, 2015

And so began day two of our adventure at Mayo Clinic.

I got a great night's sleep, but woke with a huge headache and runny nose. Seems I caught a cold from the craziness that had been the past 13 days. Not to mention, our three-year-old had been coughing in my face nonstop. All in all, though, it was a lazy morning to start.

The day was overcast, snowy and slushy. The plan was to go to Seth's appointments at Mayo and head home. Worst case scenario, we were due to arrive back home no later than 7:30 p.m. So we packed our suitcases and Seth headed outside to brush off the snow, load the bags, and get the vehicle warmed up. As I watched Seth from the warmth of the hotel room, I flashed back to college, to our wedding day when we were totally naive about marriage and life.

We were scheduled to meet with the lead eye doctor that day and knew we needed peace and quiet for his evaluation and interpretation, so Seth's cousin found a friend to watch our daughter for four hours. We left her crying, but in the hands of an obviously loving and gentle spirit, Clarisa.

Seth and I arrived at the appointment on time. Within a minute of arrival, our plan was ruined. We were told Seth needed a CT scan, pre-op appointment, and additional appointments with oncology, which meant we had a full day ahead of us and would need to stay an additional night.

His first eye exam was standard operating procedure. Then we sat in a small waiting room for a half hour before we were called in for the most important eye evaluations to date.

There we were, finally in the room where Seth's diagnosis would be validated and treatment options revealed. Only 6 in 1 million people are affected by choroidal melanoma. Because this cancer is so rare, we were sent to Mayo to meet with the nation's leading experts in its diagnosis and treatment.

We saw a female doctor and med student first. That appointment was ridiculously long in and of itself. Before the exam, she took a thorough medical history during which I texted Seth's mom to verify family history of eye problems, cancer, and various ages at time of death. The eye exam began. I continued to request and receive family history via text. My mind flashed back, yet again, to college, to our wedding day when we had no clue of what was to come, when we said "I do" to "in sickness and in health." This is what "in sickness" meant. And I couldn't help but see my mother-in-law's baby boy reclined in that chair. Who imagines their baby boy getting cancer? Who would ever wish that for their child? I couldn't help but believe that her precious cargo was in my care. Ensuring a proper family history had been gathered was the least I could do.

The room was silent as the doctor completed her examination, then took notes on photographs that had been taken of Seth's right eye the day before. Photographs, then notes. Photographs, then notes. All in complete silence. She apologized for how long it was taking. "The doctor is just very thorough. He likes things teed up when he comes in."

A little talk of Seth's work and minions lightened the air.

The doctor asked Seth if he ever had flashing in his left eye. "No," he said. She kept examining the left eye. When she was finally done, Seth said, "It makes me nervous that you were looking so long in the left eye...that you found something." (His right eye is the one with cancer). "Yes, I did," she said. "It looks like we might need to have something lasered off."

After the doctor completed her evaluation, the head doctor entered and introduced himself. He was scholarly, professor-like and clearly an all-around genius. As Dr. P evaluated Seth, I was reminded how grateful I am for genius minds. I'd be clueless if I tried such a profession. And I couldn't bear the weight of responsibility for someone's sight.

The room was silent.

Dr. P began examining Seth's eyes.

"Did you ever weld?"

"Did you ever get hit in your eyes?"

He probed further about family history. I sent more texts to Seth's mom.

As Dr. P continued to examine Seth in silence, I began to feel a little sick, the same sick I'd felt that first day we received the news. Dr. P continued his directions to Seth.

"Straight up. Down and right. To the right. Down and right."

He dictated as the female doctor scribbled notes and sketched on a piece of paper.

I found myself nearly losing it during that evaluation, during those moments of silence and seriousness. But I braced myself and made it through.

A nurse came in. "Patient has a CT scan at 2:00, last of the day. They need him down there ASAP."

The doctor verified we'll take as long as we need, finished the examination, and shared his findings.

1. The melanoma is medium-sized.

2. It is in a position where we could choose to do a

biopsy, but risks seemed to outweigh the benefits, so we decided against a biopsy. The doctor has no doubt this is melanoma.

3. There is a 90% chance of killing the tumor, saving the eye, and saving some level of vision in the eye.

4. There is a 25% chance that melanoma will show up in another part of Seth's body at some point in the future.

5. Treatment will include surgery and focused radiation to the right eye. Surgery and placement of radiation on day one, surgery and removal of radiation on day five. In hospital a total of five days.

6. There is a weak area in the left eye that also needs laser treatment.

7. There will be vision loss in the right eye. The amount of loss is unknown until post-surgery and radiation.

8. Seth will be working with one good eye from here on out. Therefore, he'll need to wear side-shielded glasses for mowing and snowblowing, polycarbonite glasses, and will not be able to wear contacts.

9. Eye will be really swollen for a month. He "won't want to work" for two to three weeks post-surgery (although Seth wants to return to work as soon as he's able). His eye will be drier than normal. His eyelid may be droopier and double vision is common, but we won't know either of those things until post-op. Both are correctable with additional surgeries if needed.

10. Follow-up appointments at Mayo one-month post-op and three months post-op.

I glanced at the notebook of questions we'd written down before we arrived. We needed to get to the CT scan ASAP, so we verified the basics and moved on out. We were escorted down the hallway by a nurse who gave us a folder of information and explained a bunch of procedures for Seth's upcoming surgeries, radiation, and hospital stay. Then, we were set free to the CT scan.

At this point, things quickly became foggy and blurry. I felt scattered. I wasn't able to focus. At all.

Seth made his way to the CT scan.

I ran to the info desk so they could point me in the direction of 15-minute parking. Clarisa, the woman who had been watching our daughter the past four hours, needed to get to work, so we agreed she'd drop her off at the main Mayo entrance. I ran across the slushy streets and saw Clarisa getting our three-year-old out of the car. They'd made a trip to Toys 'R Us, so our daughter had Valentines, a doctor kit, and stickers. Clarisa tried to get the car seat out with no success; then I tried, thankfully with success. Clarisa helped me get our daughter, her stuff, and the car seat into Mayo. I thanked Clarisa and God for her help. There's no way a three-year-old would have tolerated the past four hours.

I lugged our stuff over to the info desk and tried to orient myself as best as possible. I was still lost in another world. In fact, I wasn't hearing right or processing straight. Everything sounded muffled. The attendant at the info desk gave me a numbered plastic chip in exchange for the car seat and what sounded like a set of super complex directions to the CT scan building. All I heard was "downstairs," so my daughter and I headed down the nearest flight of stairs. I imagined her falling down the flight in a bloody mess at the bottom and walked in front of her with my hand out just in case. Live piano music streamed from the main floor. Balm for my weary soul.

I made my way to the lower level information desk for further direction. Thank God for information desks. He pointed me that way, then that way, then up.

The building was swarming with people. Sick people everywhere. Wheelchairs everywhere. We passed a baby on the way. Her life was fresh, hopeful, welcomed amongst the dying.

"We're crabby. We're late for all of our appointments," exclaimed a woman as we waited for the elevator to the CT scan. A man joked about his weight, his health. We laughed a bit. Humor was necessary, even if for a second.

By the time our daughter and I got to the imaging department, Seth had already finished preliminary preparations and was back in the waiting area. Our daughter wanted to do Valentines right then and there. A whole waiting room of people turned our direction as she loudly proclaimed, "I wanna do valentines!" I was done. DONE. I knew a lady nearby was watching my every move, my every response. And I didn't care. I knew she knew this was all a bit much for me. We escaped and decided to wait in the hallway instead. Our daughter broke out her Valentines, I wrote in my journal, and Seth was called back.

After the CT scan, we headed for a late lunch in the cafeteria, but it was closed. So we made our way down a long hallway to a bunch of fast food joints. We were supposed to be heading home by now, but we still had appointments and more tomorrow, too. We took time to contact the families who were caring for our two oldest children and told them it'd be another night.

We approached Dairy Queen. Half-priced customer appreciation day. Score. Total for three hot dogs, two Blizzards, and a sundae? $9.65. A young, beautiful woman fed her non-verbal, wheelchair-bound father figure some ice cream. It was totally unexpected in the middle of that tiny DQ, but totally beautiful.

After stuffing down a hot dog and Blizzard and rushing to Seth's pre-op appointment, our daughter and I found ourselves in yet another waiting room. She wanted to know if I could "help [her] do Valentines at the hotel." I was getting texts from my sister, my parents, from the family watching our daughter back home, from the family watching our son back home. I sighed, then took a breath. A patient on oxygen smiled at me. A Mayo employee escorted an elderly woman back for an EKG, warmly assuring her, "You can relax on this test," after the woman confessed, "It's been a long day."

Piano music played quietly in the background. I wrote in my journal.

Life is an ongoing melody. Whether we're living or dying, healthy or unhealthy, hating our life or loving our life, life plays on.

At 4:35, an elderly man darted in looking for his wife. He was "anxious for [their] 4:40 p.m. shuttle." Within seconds, she returned to the waiting room. It was the woman who'd confessed earlier, "It's been a long day." "Hurry," exclaimed her husband. She shuffled to him as fast as she could. He held open her red coat, she slid in her arms, and off they went.

A familiar melody played in the background. This was painful but beautiful. All at once.

I took a few deep breaths and peered into the hallway where people were pushing wheelchairs. Another day at Mayo was coming to an end.

Seth's appointment was going unusually long, so my daughter and I meandered into the atrium. A doctor dressed in scrubs played the piano. We sat. We rested. And I watched her play this beautiful melody of life, of living, of dying, of being in this world. The melody of living amidst the dying.

4

CAREGIVING, SURRENDERING, AND A GOLD BOTTLE CAP PLAQUE

February 1, 2015

The third day at Mayo Clinic, I found myself feeling a little helpless.

We entered the oncology waiting area for the first of two back-to-back appointments Seth had scheduled that morning. The waiting area was loaded, filled with sick people. Our daughter was coughing again, and I'd learned my lesson on coughing once that week already. Seth suggested that we should go to the atrium where it was quiet. He'd wait alone in the waiting room.

So off we went. Our daughter and I parked on a couch, and I plopped all our stuff on a nearby chair. In that moment, I felt helpless. I recognized this feeling from days gone by, from my sister's many years battling addiction and mental illness. Yes, there's a helplessness that can settle in for caregivers after a while. A time comes when you wonder if you're really doing any good, if you're really worth any while. I knew this feeling because I'd lived it. I have, in fact, learned to flee from it. Because not being able to do anything for a loved one is heartbreaking and mind numbing. It makes you want to surrender and say forget it; there's nothing I have to offer. Yes, I allowed myself to sit in that caregiver helplessness in the Mayo atrium a minute or two that day. I felt for a moment that it was pointless for me and my daughter to sit there, far from Seth and his oncology appointments.

But this day, God graced me with His viewpoint.

In came a wife pushing her husband in a wheelchair. I'd noticed them the day prior when we were waiting for Seth's CT scan, and now today in oncology. She talked on the phone as she pushed her husband to the windowed wall of the atrium. She helped him out of his wheelchair into a regular chair, all the while continuing to talk on the phone. He sat in silence, weak and frail. After a while, she handed the phone to her husband, promptly picked up another phone, and began texting. When she was done texting, she broke out a tablet and took some notes, then reviewed what I assumed was a letter detailing what was next on the day's agenda for her husband. He passed her the phone. And she assisted him back in his wheelchair. Off they went, back to oncology. *Yes, this is the role of the caregiver – calling, emailing, texting, pushing, prodding, encouraging, lifting, loving, and verifying this and that. Caregivers manage relationships and medical realities.*

I see God. Caregiving isn't pointless. There's purpose here. There's a reason we've been assigned to this role. Even when it's hard. Even when it feels like there's nothing we can do to help.

After 2 1/2 hours and two appointments with oncology, Seth returned with updates, news, and pictures of a gold bottle cap called a plaque. During surgery, Dr. P will be temporarily stitching the gold plaque to the wall of Seth's right eye where the tumor is located. Focused radiation will be delivered to the eye over the course of a five-day hospital stay.

Clearly, this gold bottle cap plaque is out of my hands. From a medical standpoint, there's nothing I can do to help with the events that are about to transpire. I'll leave that to Dr. P and his colleagues at Mayo.

But I am caregiver. I can be there when Seth gets out of surgery. I can sit by his side when they take the bandages off for the first time, the second time, the third time, and the fourth. I can drive him home when we're discharged. I can make our home comfortable for him. I can write, text, make phone calls, and respond to Facebook messages to ensure everyone's updated along the way. I can keep the kids out of Daddy's hair so he can rest and heal. I can be there for him on the hard days, when doubt and discouragement settle in. I can be positive and supportive when all I really want to do is run and hide. I can believe with him. I can believe for him. I can believe in him. I can love him. I can pray for him. I can surrender my husband's healing to Jesus, to a mighty God who can and will heal him. And I can rest in peace knowing this role of caregiver has been assigned to me more than once so my eyes might be opened, so my heart might be enlarged, so my faith might be strengthened, so I might understand what it means to trust and love. Even when. Even if. Even so.

5

RADIATED: HOSPITAL
TIME LAPSE DAY ONE

February 2, 2015

8:55 a.m.

I'm eating Oreo cookies for breakfast this morning. Why not?
We've been at the hospital since 7:30 a.m. We're officially
admitted. Now we're waiting. The chaplain's already been in
to visit. Just so happens he's brother-in-law to Seth's frater-
nity brother. Seth admits to the chaplain that he feels unusually strong; perhaps it's because he's being carried by a strong
support system of loved ones and prayer warriors. As I continue to chomp on the familiar chocolate and cream, I stare at
the pain assessment scales in this PRE-pre-op waiting room. A
patient sobs across the way. I try to listen in to determine the
weight of her burdens, but I can't hear detail, only cries.

1:14 p.m.

Seth and I were separated at 10:11 a.m. when he was wheeled
in to pre-op, I joined Seth's parents in the family waiting area,

and shortly after we were directed to the hospital room where Seth will be staying for the next five days. While we were eating lunch in the cafeteria, I received word that Seth had gone into surgery. Placement of the gold bottle cap plaque that will deliver radiation to his right eye for the next five days was an hour shorter than we expected so we were a little surprised when a nurse called us to join Dr. P for a post-op consult at 12:50 p.m.

Dr. P had two images of Seth's eye and the cancerous area printed for us. He said everything "went really well," that the gold bottle cap plaque is "perfectly placed and perfectly positioned." The resident doctor will change the eye patch and shield and is the only one allowed to do so. Dr. P will be in every day to visit. Seth is allowed to go walking around the hospital every day after 3:00 p.m. as long as he's accompanied by one of us. We need to hold him by the hand or arm, and he's to look front and straight ahead. No scanning allowed. No reading is allowed this week either. Seth can watch TV from a distance, but nothing up close that would require his eyes to scan. He's to remain well hydrated, and the doctor wants him to eat a lot of APPLES while he's here. Apparently, my titling of this series, "The Apple of My Eye," is right on for more than one reason.

So now, we wait again. Seth is in recovery. His dad is napping in the room. His mom is getting coffee. And I'm here in the family waiting area. The family next to me is here for cancer, too. They're discussing a kind 80-year-old woman who was up praying for their family first thing this morning. They comment on her kindness, her sweetness. Seth's mom returns, and we talk about health, wellness, and nutrition until Seth's dad notifies us that Seth will be on his way to the room soon.

3:05 p.m.

Seth was just brought to the room from recovery. He's still waking up from anesthesia, but persisted that he was "starving," so the nurse got him peanut butter toast. The nurse gently reminded him he'll want to eat a lot of apples. Seth's reported more than once already that his eye is "more irritated than he expected it to be." And now, he's sleeping. I have a whole pile of tasks I brought to do while we're here this week, but I can't imagine getting my brain around any of it right now. I think I'll read a mindless magazine.

4:33 p.m.

The nurse recently administered Seth pain medication at his request. His eye is throbbing. "Like daggers," he said. Seth said it's "not good to open [his] eyes." Unless he "keeps looking straight ahead, it hurts. The scratchiness is painful like gravel or sandpaper." It feels better to keep both of his eyes closed, so for now, he's continuing to sleep. Seth's youngest brother is on his way for a visit, and Seth's parents found him a DVD player so he can watch movies in the room once he's up to it.

5:07 p.m.

I'm nearing the end of Jennie Allen's book, Restless.[1] I've been plodding through it since the plane ride home from a writing conference four months ago. I'd just begun chapter 21, "When Women Dream," when I became keenly aware of the steady beeping of machines in the hospital room. I looked at Seth sleeping, his right eye covered with a patch, bandages, and metal shield. I thought about everything that's transpired in my life, even in just the past six weeks. And I have to believe that ALL of this is part of God's plan. There's mystery in not knowing. If we allow ourselves to live aware, the threads start lining up, weaving into fabric that makes complete sense.

The machine keeps on beeping. Life keeps on ticking. We breathe in. We breathe out. We can cling to our way or surrender to God's way. We choose. And what I'm learning is that if we refuse God's way, He prods us gently, sometimes not-so gently. Go this way. This is the way. Sometimes it takes a major meltdown in the midst of a dream come true.

Sometimes it takes life-altering circumstances to turn us in the right direction. But when we surrender to God's beat, His plan, life is better. It just is.

7:59 p.m.

Around 7:30 p.m., Seth began complaining about his eye again. He wasn't sure the pain medication they administered shortly after 4:00 p.m. was really working. He was having a hard time imagining lying in a hospital room with his eyes closed, in pain and discomfort for five days. His brother and I suggested that maybe they could administer a stronger pain med, so when the nurse came in, we made the request and it was granted. Within 15 minutes, the newer, stronger pain medication had set in and Seth was chatting away, the most energetic he'd been all day. He talked with his brother about beards and how he looked like an "albino seal" when he shaved his off at Christmas. And he joked about his eye. "When I snuck a peek in the mirror, I was expecting a horror show, but all I saw was an eye patch." Yep, that's my man.

We walked two laps around the unit. It was the first time he'd been up and out of bed since he sat in the wheelchair at 10:11 this morning. Then we turned down the heat, got him snuggled back in bed with his fleece blanket, and prepared to leave. He was fading fast, but in good spirits.

10:32 p.m.

I'm back in the hotel room finishing the day's updates. I might not make it through the five books, February budget, or anything else I brought to do this week, but we made it through another day. That's all we ever need to do.

6

MOURNING AND REJOICING IN SICKNESS AND IN HEALTH

February 3, 2015

My Meyers-Briggs personality type is INFJ. That means if left to myself, I have a natural tendency to go deep and dark. I take life seriously, sometimes too seriously. I analyze, over-analyze, sense everything, and am deeply intuitive. And I have absolutely no problem lingering in quiet, isolated spaces. By myself.

God created me to be introspective. But that doesn't mean He wants me to be alone all the time.

Throughout this journey through eye cancer, God has reminded me that I can't face this alone. In fact, I'm pretty sure He's been saying to me for a while now that I can't do life alone, either. Yes, that's hard to admit. After my travels to Haiti and the Dominican Republic, I realized that Americans are incredibly independent and self-sufficient. For the most part, we have what we need. And we are busy. Very busy. Always doing something. Always going somewhere.

So on a surface level, we don't really need each other to survive. It's easy to become prideful, disconnected, too busy for real living and authentic connection. To be completely honest? I'm not sure my personality lines up with mainstream American culture.

But sometimes, I have to step back and let life take its course. I have to let God run with it and surround me with community even when I'd rather stay in a room by myself, reading and writing all day.

Today was no exception. God showed me what it looks like to linger in community, in mourning and rejoicing, in sickness and in health.

All in all, it was a good day. Yes.

Seth's parents and I arrived at the hospital by 8:15 a.m. Seth's youngest brother arrived shortly after.

For those of you who prayed for Seth's comfort, let me say that his pain was much more manageable today. Overnight, they landed on a pain management "cocktail" that seems to be working well. Seth mentioned pain and discomfort a couple times today, but not nearly as much as yesterday.

I ordered Seth breakfast and we chatted a bit. After breakfast, Seth decided he wanted to put his clothes on for the first time since surgery, so everyone left and I helped him get out of his hospital gown and into a loose-fitting t-shirt and basketball shorts. We snapped a couple photos with his eye patch, then when his parents and brother came back, we enjoyed some laughs as Seth and I composed a Facebook status in our annoyingly perfectionistic, both first born, now old married couple way. I typed the post and got it up on Facebook for Seth. Within minutes, comments started flowing in. His mom read the assortment of lovely, encouraging, and occasionally funny comments throughout the day.

Seth said as he sat in bed, "This is nice, guys. Coffee. Comfortable chairs. You guys talking to me."

Then we pulled up a special, heartfelt message Seth and I had recently received. Seth's mom and I tag teamed reading of the post as Seth, his dad, and brother listened. We spent time reflecting on the loving words and the thoughtful individual who wrote them.

The guys told jokes about Metamucil and bed pans, ice fishing and Seth's seafood allergy. Seth called the nurse the "drug lady" when she came in, and she gently reminded him she'd prefer to be called a "therapeutic manager." My mom, her best friend, and our three-year-old FaceTimed us from home and Seth's cousin called for a chat.

Seth said again, "It's nice to have all these guys here. They're talking. And I can just listen."

Seth's brother left and I grabbed lunch with Seth's mom. After we got back to the room, our flower girl came to visit. She's now a doctoral student at Mayo Clinic specializing in proton therapy with aspirations to become a medical physicist. (Yes, we're old and not nearly as smart as our flower girl.) We chatted about everyday things and surgery things, but we also talked about not-so-everyday things that only a person in the medical field would know. She educated us, sharing that the gold bottle cap plaque delivering radiation to Seth's eye this week would be reused later down the road by another patient, that there were three medical physicists in Seth's surgery, and that he'll be surveyed for the presence of radioactive seeds before he leaves the hospital on Friday. She reminded us that "positivity is half the battle" and Seth agreed, stating, "there have been very few moments when I have lost my positive attitude." Yes, that is true. I am married to a VERY positive man.

My sister called, we watched a movie in the quiet of the hospital room with Seth's parents, and we FaceTimed our two oldest when they got home from school.

All in all, our second day in the hospital was good. But what struck me most was the community, the gathering of loved ones who came around us in our time of need.

When we stand in front of family and friends vowing to love and cherish "in sickness and in health," the truth is, we have no idea what that sickness is going to look like. Will it be infertility, diabetes, cancer, traumatic brain injury, stroke, disability, heart attack, mental illness, or plain old stomach flu? It's hard to say. What I'm thinking today is that YES, wedding vows are of course important, holy and to be kept. But what if we ALL vowed to love and cherish each other in sickness and in health? What if we ALL came around each other not just in sickness, but in health, too? What if we created authentic, meaningful community in all seasons of life? Wouldn't life make a lot more sense? Wouldn't we feel a lot more relief at the end of each day?

This verse comes to mind...

"Rejoice with those who rejoice; mourn with those who mourn." - Romans 12:15

It's basically a reiteration of "in sickness and in health." What if we lived like that? What if?

Tonight, I leave you with that. Tomorrow, day three.

Good night, friends.

7

WHEN BEAUTY FALLS

February 4, 2015

Let me just start off by saying thank you for checking in. Maybe you're a friend or family member, maybe you're a fellow writer or regular follower of mine, maybe you just happened to land on this story via Google search. Whoever you are, thank you for joining our journey.

Today was day three in the hospital. It was a good day, as status quo as a day in the hospital could be. Seth was in good spirits. The gold bottle cap plaque is still stitched in his eye. The radiation is still working to kill the cancer. The cocktail of pain medications they created for him two nights ago is still working well. Seth's still eating two apples a day. And Dr. P is fabulously kind and intelligent. Seth lapped the unit three times holding hands with me this afternoon. And he enjoyed an awesome piece of wedding-worthy cake I brought him from a bakery in Mayo's basement. Perhaps the worst part of his day was when he admitted he'd be lonely when we left the hospital at 7:00 p.m.

You see, Seth and I have these terms of agreement we've landed on in our 20 years together. When I'm down, he's usually up. And when he's down, I'm usually up. With that in mind, Seth's day was good. My day turned from shaky to profoundly holy.

For all of you who are curious about the big-picture beyond the four walls of Seth's hospital room, stay with me. I'm about to share more about my day. Although you must know, I'm certain words won't do it justice.

Let's begin, shall we?

I got out of bed a little later than I'd wanted, but still managed to run over to Starbucks for a cup of coffee and scone for Seth before the shuttle came to pick us up. Let me just say, I was fine at this point. But I wasn't awesome. We've been arriving at the hospital by 8:15 a.m. and leaving at 7:00 p.m. I've been writing each night after we get back, which has left me staying up extra late to get in a little quiet time alone before doing the day all over again. I haven't exercised for five days, which is too long without a workout for me. I've been sleeping and feeling fine from all indications, but perhaps stress has accumulated under the surface without my awareness.

While I was waiting for coffee at Starbucks, I received an email. It humbled me, hurt my heart a bit, and required an immediate response. While the issue was resolved within a few hours, I'm sharing because I believe it was critical to the start and storyline of my day.

We arrived at the hospital and took the elevator up to Seth's room. I went right in, and Seth's parents headed straight for coffee and the waiting room. Seth was still sleeping, so I broke out my laptop and began drafting a response to the email I'd received earlier. I had the email completely drafted by the time Seth woke up, but didn't send it quite yet. I got Seth his coffee and scone, ordered his breakfast, and set up his bed tray so it would be ready when the food was delivered. But Seth noticed right away that something wasn't right. He questioned, "Is something wrong? I can't see well, but my other senses are making up for my lack of sight. I can tell something's not right with you today." I told him vaguely what had happened, then shared, "I think I'm just more tired than I know. Or it's all piling up on me or something."

We decided to get Seth a shower before breakfast arrived, so I broke out the hand-held shower head and Seth sat down on a chair in the bathroom, clothes and all, for his first post-surgery hair washing. I had to take off my shoes and socks so my feet didn't get wet, and I know this sounds weird, but it all felt a little Jesus-y. I wasn't in the mood to get wet and take my shoes and socks off. And truth be told, I'm the farthest from a hair stylist there is. But this felt like something Jesus would do. I love my husband and it was time for a washing. So I washed his hair and helped him get in the shower before I let him be.

I finished composing my email and pressed send. Breakfast arrived. Seth got out of the shower and asked me to read the last two days of posts I'd published. He usually reads my posts quietly at his leisure. Sometimes he comments, sometimes he doesn't. With him not being able to read this week, he hasn't read any of my writing. I was feeling blah and raw, and for some reason, I wasn't sure if I could make it through a reading of my own writing. So when Seth suggested maybe his mom could read the posts to him later, it was a definite yes.

Seth's parents returned to the room. Within a couple minutes, we got a call from Dr. P's secretary. Seth's short-term disability paperwork had been signed, was over at Mayo, and needed to be picked up in person and sent to Seth's employer ASAP. But a form I'd signed yesterday caused a whole lot of commotion, which meant that before I'd be able to pick up the paperwork from Mayo, I'd need to go sign more paperwork downstairs at the hospital.

The day wasn't going smoothly so far.

I took the folder of paperwork and went downstairs to begin resolving our paperwork problem. I completed a new form and went back up to the room to have Seth sign it. At that point, Seth's mom was ready to begin reading my posts, so it was a good time for me to bring the paperwork back downstairs and leave for a little quiet time.

Off I went. I returned the paperwork to the powers that be and let myself wander through the hospital.

I passed the row of nun portraits I'd seen two days prior and read the plaque that described Mayo's history, how one nun dreamed of opening a hospital after a tornado back in the 1800s. Look at this place now.

I meandered through the gift shop with my eyes set on beautiful things. Flower bouquets. Handmade dolls. Delicate earrings. And plaques with words that would someday mean the world to somebody.

I followed the sign to the chapel. All the way up, down, and around long hallways.

As I turned the corner into the chapel, a husband photographed his wife signing the cross across her chest.

A woman sat near the front, completely still, completely silent.

I was now one of three in the enormous Mayo chapel.

The chapel was incredible, amazing, breathtakingly beautiful. I sat in a pew and let my eyes scan wherever they may. I didn't pray so much as I experienced God's presence. Light shone through yellow and blue stained-glass windows. I stared at vanilla cream columns and thoughtfully painted blue and white floral designs on window arches way up high. I noted the repetitive rectangular design on the ceiling, the fans, and golden chandeliers. When a young woman wheeled an elderly woman through the chapel, I noticed the stations of the cross, the paintings lining the walls.

What I noticed most was the light coming in through the stained-glass windows, the shifting of light and shadows, first on the floor, then throughout the whole chapel. The light wasn't predictable. But it was soft, beautiful. Unlike the world's rude and unforgiving ways, the light was gentle and forgiving. It entered subtly and slowly. I had to wait for it. I never knew where it would land next. A shifting of light here meant a shadow there. Freshly lit spaces were stunning

and radiant in modest, unassuming ways. I likened the light
to God's ways, to the Spirit's movement in my life. I need to
learn these rhythms of grace.

When my soul felt rested, I got up, walked around the stations of the cross, and examined the paintings.

In the back of the chapel, I found a large Bible on a ped-
estal. It was opened to Matthew. The treasure and the pearl.[1]
Jesus Feeds Five Thousand.[2] Jesus Walks on the Water.[3] Other
Miracles. Hmmm...of all the pages. I've been hearing these
messages of feeding five thousand and walking on water
repeatedly the past year and a half. And now here, at Mayo.
God has been speaking messages of faith and obedience, provision and trust.

I returned to Seth's room. My soul felt much more settled. The chaplain came for a visit and we chatted some more.
But before long, we realized I'd need to make my way over
to Mayo Clinic to pick up that paperwork. So off to the
shuttle I went.

The shuttle ride was humbling. At the Ronald McDonald
House, a mama loaded her significantly disabled son onto the
shuttle. At the Gift of Life transplant house, a woman wearing a scarf with stray hairs stuffed underneath sat down in
front of me. And along the way, an unusually friendly man
engaged me, eventually revealing he's transitioning from
man to woman, how it's been hard on his wife. Dear God,
what would you have me see? What would you have me
learn? What would you have me experience? How would you
have me respond?

At that point, I was in another world as far as I was con-
cerned. I likened the experience to my time in Haiti. For some
reason, I'd been dropped in another foreign but holy place.

When I arrived at Mayo, I noted an elderly man playing
piano effortlessly in the atrium. I'd entered from the upper
street level where it was impossible to ignore the crowd of
patients and caregivers surrounding him. From the second I arrived, I sensed this was a holy place, holier than two

weeks prior when I'd noted the healing power of that piano. The man played and played. One song after another. "How Great Thou Art."[4] "His Eye is on the Sparrow."[5] On and on. A man limped with double leg braces. Men and women listened long in wheelchairs. A woman wearing bright pink nodded her head continually in agreement with the music. People threw out requests one after another. And sick people passed with caregivers. The elderly man played with eloquence, all by heart. It was incredibly, incredibly holy. From my perspective up above on street level, it was so holy that it nearly took my breath away. Tears streamed. I finally had to walk away to gather myself because the presence of God was so tangible in that space.

I took pictures. I stood still and listened. I was approached by a man in his 50s who asked my story, brought me to tears, and told me I was beautiful. I moved around from side to side as my body led. I didn't rush, but stayed still, quiet in this place of holiness. In an odd way, I wished for everyone to be here, to realize how sick we all really are, how we're living amongst the dying and dying amidst the living, how we're all desperate for the tender loving care of a Savior. It was a glimpse of heaven on earth. Ridiculously holy, indeed.

As enjoyable as this was, I had to move on. So I picked up the paperwork then meandered down the hallway to grab some lunch. I bought that tiny wedding-worthy cake from a basement bakery and walked into a quaint ladies' boutique filled with clothing and jewelry. On the way out, I thanked the store owner for bringing such beauty to a place filled with such pain. "Thank you," she said. "That means a lot to me."

On the way to the hospital four days ago, I told Seth that if I was a screenplay writer and movie director, I'd make a quiet, beautiful, emotionally complex and visually rich movie with a deeply spiritual and meaningful storyline. Yes, I'd make a movie that looks and feels like today. Its title? When Beauty Falls.

8

RANDOM THOUGHTS
FROM THE HOSPITAL

February 5, 2015

Seth's fourth day in the hospital consisted of status quo with more fatigue and more mentions of throbbing pain than the past two days. But all in all, things are well. We did receive at least one notable update from the doctor this afternoon, but I'll wait to share that until tomorrow after Seth's surgery and removal of the gold radioactive plaque.

For today, I'd like to offer a few random thoughts from the hospital. After yesterday's deep post and a long week at the hospital, light-hearted words will go a long way.

Random Thought #1

"When bad things happen, there's always someone who asks, 'Why me?' It's easy for people to compare their lives to mine and feel really sad. But this is it. I accept it. It is what it is." – Seth

Random Thought #2

FaceTime is awesome. We've used it every day this week to communicate with my mom and the kids. It's been a surprisingly great way to expose the kids to Seth's eye, patch, and shield before we come home. It's also helped maintain a bit of normalcy for our family during the hospitalization.

Random Thought #3

Hospital cafeteria food is actually quite good. Seth's parents and I have eaten most of our meals here at the hospital. Today's lunch was the best so far. Turkey. Yukon gold mashed potatoes. Gravy. Cooked carrots and snap peas. Yum.

Random Thought #4

When you're in the hospital for a whole week, visitors are a great change of pace. Our flower girl came to visit again today, as did Seth's dad's cousin and wife who live locally. All three individuals were sweet and added joy to the end of our day. Fresh perspective is welcomed and necessary.

Random Thought #5

Jimmy John's is awesome. I told Seth I was going to order Jimmy John's for dinner tonight for a change of pace. Let me tell you that the Jimmy John's dude arrived at the hospital entrance on his BIKE. The temperatures out there today are SUB-zero! I was beyond impressed. And of course, the service was speedy and the food was delicious. HUGE fan of Jimmy John's.

Random Thought #6

Facebook, Facebook Messenger, Instagram, Twitter, emails, texts, Caring Bridge, and blog comments are an awesome way to communicate with a busy CAREGIVER. Thank you, everyone, for your awesome support.

Random Thought #7

Facebook, Facebook Messenger, Instagram, Twitter, emails, texts, Caring Bridge, and blog comments are an awesome way to encourage a PATIENT. Seth has really enjoyed hearing us read the messages everyone has been leaving. Thank you!

Random Thought #8

When you're at the hospital long enough, you become accustomed to the scenery. Wheelchairs, IVs, bandages, beeping machines, scrubs, head scarves, leg braces, and the like become the norm. Sure, the sights catch you off guard once in a while, but all in all, you acclimate. I wonder what it would be like if ALL of our burdens and bruises were exposed so visibly to the world. Wouldn't we be a lot more sensitive to fellow humans?

Random Thought #9

Being at the hospital for great lengths of time can make you delirious. After returning from the hospital this evening, my father-in-law, mother-in-law, and I got a little delirious in the hotel elevator. We got in, but all three of us just stood there forgetting to select a floor so we could go up! My father-in-law made sure to let the lady in the elevator know we weren't intoxicated, we were just delirious, overly tired from a week at the hospital. Thank goodness for comedically-inclined people like my father-in-law.

Random Thought #10

If you want to do good for someone in the hospital, keep it sweet but simple. Relatives took Seth's parents out for dinner tonight and they came back with some awesome coconut cake to-go for me. Oh, my goodness. SCORE.

9

RADIATED: HOSPITAL
TIME LAPSE DAY FIVE

February 6, 2015

8:55 a.m.

We arrived at the hospital 45 minutes ago. Seth's parents went to the cafeteria to get some breakfast, and I washed Seth's hair before he took a shower. When Seth got back in bed, he noted he's gotten "in a routine that has been healing and helpful" during his stay at the hospital. Leaving "the routine of Tuesday, Wednesday and Thursday" is making him a little anxious. I have to admit, I'm a tad anxious as well. Before we know it, we'll be heading back home where our three kids will be waiting for our love and care. Seth will be out of commission for a while, so I'll be responsible for helping him while caring for the house and three kids full-time. But people have been generous with their offers of help, so we'll be fine. Seth's surgery for removal of the gold bottle cap plaque is scheduled for 10:30 a.m., but there haven't been any signs of movement yet.

10:47 a.m.

Seth was wheeled away to surgery at 9:17 a.m. By 10:40 a.m., we received word that surgery had just been completed. He'll be in recovery for a while, so we'll wait patiently in his room until he returns.

11:45 a.m.

Four nurses brought Seth back to his hospital room 10 minutes ago. They helped him into bed and got him settled. Seth reported a rating of 5 on the pain scale of 0-10. (He hadn't reported anything higher than 4 since Monday after plaque placement.) His eye was stinging and throbbing, so nurses gave him his usual cocktail of pain meds. Napping seemed the next best course of action. He was definitely still coming out of anesthesia.

11:55 a.m.

Seth had been completely silent for 10 minutes. Out of the blue, he shared, "I'm going to want a Blizzard later when I wake up." Seth's mom assured him we could make that happen. Then back to silence.

1:17 p.m.

I just got back from lunch with Seth's mom. Seth is upright in bed, and lunch is on its way. We're hoping he'll be able to tolerate the food since it's one of the requirements for discharge later this afternoon. Seth was administered his pain management cocktail at 11:45 a.m., but now he's reporting stabbing eye pain. The nurse gave him a new pain med via IV, which thankfully kicked in within a few minutes.

2:59 p.m.

I decided to watch a live stream of IF: Gathering,[1] an organization that exists to "gather, equip and unleash the next generation of women to live out their purpose." Had we not been at the hospital all week, I would've been attending a special ladies' event today and tomorrow to watch the live stream. Most of the women speaking at the event are in the heart of my writing niche, so I was excited to catch even a few minutes of it live.

Angie Smith[2] interviewed a woman who lost her husband and two boys in a tornado. The woman spoke, "I'm here today. I have a choice to live in sorrow and let their lives be completely wasted, or I can talk about what God did. I chose Him in my darkest hour." Then Jennie Allen,[3] founder of IF:Gathering, spoke. "We're in the wilderness bumping up against each other wondering what we're supposed to do. We are at war and the prize is faith. I believe that women are going to move from journals of sight to lives of faith." I love my sister writers. They're so wise. Yes, let's share what God's done in our lives. Let's live by faith and not by sight. The themes fit this eye cancer journey and everything else transpiring in life these days.

4:20 p.m.

I went downstairs to the pharmacy to pick up three prescriptions Seth will need once he's home. When I got back up to the room, Seth said he might be discharged soon. He inquired about getting an additional prescription for pain medication, so the nurse is talking to the doctor. I just washed Seth's hair for the second time today; we'll be heading to a hotel for the night and it'll be hard to protect his eyes from water with the layout of the bathroom there. Exhaustion is setting in. Big time.

6:24 p.m.

Seth was officially discharged and walked out the doors of his hospital room at 5:03 p.m. We took a shuttle back to the hotel, then his mom and I went to Mayo to pick up the fourth prescription. While we were there, we verified with one of Dr. P's colleagues that Seth can resume reading as he feels comfortable. We'd forgotten to ask at discharge.

9:56 p.m.

We enjoyed a casual dinner with Seth's parents before saying thank you and good-bye. So here we are. In the hotel room. I'm writing and Seth's sleeping. We stayed here together on Sunday night before Seth's surgery, I've been alone in the room all week, and now tonight, we're right back where we started. Radiation was delivered to Seth's eye for five days straight via the gold bottle cap plaque while he was in the hospital. Now the only physical evidence he's been through eye cancer treatment is a big eye patch and shield, and a bunch of stitches nobody will ever see except the doctors.

One month from now, we'll return to Mayo Clinic. Dr. P will take a look at the stitches to make sure they're dissolving as expected. He'll examine Seth's eyes, and perhaps we'll get a glimpse of the impact radiation has had on Seth's sight in his right eye. He'll check for double vision and if there's any drooping of the eyelid, both common with this surgery. Three months after that, we'll return for another appointment. Dr. P will examine Seth's vision again, but will also begin looking at the tumor to see if it's shrinking. Four months post radiation is the earliest they'd expect to see shrinkage. If, at that time, the tumor is shrinking, they'll see Seth in 6-8 months. If, at that time, the tumor is the same size or bigger, they'll see him every 3 months until it's smaller.

When we wake up in the morning, we'll be heading home. Seth will be out of work all next week. If all goes as planned, he'll be working from home the last two weeks of February. Once we've acclimated to home, I'll touch base with another update.

Thank you for your faithful prayers, your love and support while we've been in the hospital. You're the best, and we're so grateful.

I'm exhausted, friends. Good night.

10

WHAT NO NORMAL
LOOKS LIKE FROM HERE

February 9, 2015

Words turned into sentences. And sentences turned into paragraphs. That's when I knew it was time to write again. It had only been 60 hours since I published last, but it felt like a week. Yes, that's how I always know it's time to free the wild beast of my brain that's constantly moving, constantly drafting, constantly writing the inner and outer-workings of life.

We arrived back home to relative peace and quiet that Saturday, long before the oldest two dazzled the doorway with energy from basketball and a birthday party. "Welcome Home Dad" was strung across the mud room wall. The floors were clean, the counters pristine. A "Get Well Soon" balloon floated above the kitchen island along with Elmo and a Valentine heart. Seth's favorite treats – Reese's cups, Reese's Pieces, and Diet Coke – sat next to a yellow plant that was about to bloom. Two Valentine's boxes had been crafted with care for classroom parties. Chocolate chip cookies and frosted pink cupcakes filled our countertops. Mom made the place comfortable while we were gone.

Seth went straight for a nap along with our three-year-old. I sat, wrote a bit, did who knows what. My body felt slow. I wasn't sure what to do or where I fit in this nothing's-normal-anymore home of mine. Seven and a half weeks had passed since I wrapped up the last day of my 14 ½ year career as a speech-language therapist, but new normal never had a chance to set in. We had no clue, NO CLUE, we'd be facing cancer when we decided six months ago I'd stop working to stay home and pursue dreams of writing and photography. But now, yes now, I was here, in no normal land, back home after my husband's week-long eye cancer treatment. I let myself sit. Just sit. This wasn't normal. It was new.

Nap time passed and our oldest arrived back home from basketball. Seth woke from his groggy slumber, we made a dinner of the week's leftovers, then he promptly returned to bed. He apologized to our son, as he'd promised him movie night on the couch, but he just couldn't. He needed to sleep. So I tucked our youngest into bed and spent some quality time with our son as best as I could. I'd never take dad's place, but one parent's better than none.

I woke early the next day, before the crack of dawn. Our youngest was awake, loud and a little needy. Seth was asleep, quiet and a little irritated with all the noise and activity. I brought our three-year-old down to play and do whatever, because that's what I could handle. This would've been a church day, but our son needed to get to basketball again and our oldest daughter needed to be picked up from a sleepover. So we took a pass on church, even though I needed it.

I'd changed Seth's eye patch and shield that morning. His eye was puffy, really puffy. Itchy, really itchy. We weren't sure why, so he took pain meds and got back into bed for a long day of rest.

A friend brought a crock pot of spaghetti sauce, cookies, and oranges peeled, ready to go. Thank God, I thought. I hate cooking and was in no mood to do so considering the circumstances. Seth greeted our visitor briefly, stayed long enough to eat, then called it a wrap. He went back upstairs, and I put the leftovers away for another day.

The rest of the day was haphazard, semi-restful at best. The kids played and watched too much TV. I did a little this and a little that, picking up laundry, putting dishes in the washer, gathering piles of Polly Pockets our youngest had strewn across the couch. I longed for normalcy, for any new normal, so during nap time, I reopened books for the business that's closing slower than expected, then invited the kids to play Uno (color and number matching for the win).

Seth slept and slept some more. I kept checking on him, but he wanted nothing but to stay in bed. Occasionally, I'd enter our room and he'd be in bed with headphones on, listening to a podcast or catching up on *Game of Thrones*. But sleep was his activity of choice. So I let him be until 9:30 when I invited him down for *Walking Dead* followed by a night cap of pain meds.

Morning came again. With it, a glimpse of normalcy. Seth woke with our youngest at 5:45. I put drops of healing ointment in Seth's eye, then refreshed the patch and shield with the breathable tape I'd grown to love somehow. It was a noisy, hurried morning. Seth asked us to leave the bedroom. He couldn't handle the volume nor the activity so I closed the door, took the kids downstairs, and left him to sleep, rest, and recover. I fed three kids, made cold lunches, and packed their bags tight. Off he went. Off she went. And off I went with our youngest to the gym for exercise that keeps me on the straight and narrow when all else fails.

I made my way around the track, two times, maybe three, then plopped on an elliptical. I needed this. Bad. I weighed myself this morning for the first time in a week or two. A new non-pregnancy high. When I left my career seven and a half weeks ago, I was already at a non-pregnancy high because of all the stress and chaos. Now after an eye cancer diagnosis, trip with Compassion International, days of eye cancer appointments, and a week-long hospitalization for my husband? Another new high. I was now 10 pounds higher than my pre-pregnancy weight with baby #3 four years ago. Ugh. I'd worked hard with a personal trainer to get to that pre-pregnancy weight. But still. 10 pounds up from that. Ugh. Grace, indeed. Today's workout wasn't for my weight. It was for my mental health. For the wellness of my being, not the perfection of my physique.

The workout was slow to start. I felt the weight of my body, soul, and mind as I moved my feet back and forth on the elliptical. I started slow, eager to go faster as my body led. I pressed forward, next on my iPod, letting the Spirit move to music that soothed my soul and felt in line with who I am now. "Let it Go."[1] A little Adele.[2] A Christmas song for good measure. Whatever.

I noticed the woman to my right, the one I've been watching a year or two, the one I wave to, say hi to, the one I'd be friends with given any proper opportunity. Yes, there was the woman who inspired me most in this place, the one who throws punches and kicks fierce, the one whose pain shows through, the one whose dreads fall long and fly where they may as she dances to her own beat on the treadmill. YES, anywhere she pleases. She dances, kicks, punches, exhales CH-CH-CH, CH-CH-CH, as long as her soul needs to heal, breathe, and bring forth life.

Time had passed, more than I knew. So I got off the elliptical and back on the track. I passed the woman throwing punches and prayed we'd become friends someday. As I slowed to cool, I approached a man I've been sharing the track with for a year or two, a man who walks slowly and initiates conversation awkwardly, but who's always ready to chat, even for a bit. He was slower than normal, so much so I could barely keep pace. I knew right away something was wrong. I was right. He's been diagnosed with Progressive Supranuclear Palsy. They think it might have something to do with his exposure to agent orange in Vietnam War. He's headed back to the VA hospital later this week for more testing. He's not sure what they're going to do, but his daily exercise around the track has improved his health and extended his life in remarkable ways. They've taken away his driver's license, and for that, he's notably saddened and disturbed. I walked slowly and let him talk through the pain. He wants to sell everything and move south so he can walk and bike in air that's comfortable. I heard him out and wished him well more than once before we parted ways. Athletes passed us, running as if life is a sprint. I'm not sprinting anymore. An unpredictable snail's pace is fine. Just fine for me, I say.

I returned home with our youngest. The house was silent. Seth was still sleeping.

Our three-year-old climbed up on the bed and begged daddy for McDonald's. "No. I just want to sleep today." But before long, he was up, ready to go – for our daughter, I supposed.

Seth's eyes hurt from the sun. He felt nauseous. He just wanted to go back home and back to bed. But he pressed on anyway. He ate the "just okay" grilled chicken sandwich I ordered him for a healthy dose of protein, and hugged our three-year-old tight when she tucked into his side.

And when we returned home, he slept. The three-year-old baby slept. I wrote the words that had been turning into sentences, the sentences that had been turning into paragraphs. And I waited for the after-school rush of loud, vibrant, no normal.

11

SLEEPING, DREAMING, AND DAYDREAMING

February 11, 2015

Since we arrived home from the hospital, many have asked me how Seth's doing. My default reply is that he's been sleeping a lot. So yeah, I guess he's doing okay? Seth slept 75% to 95% of the time the first two days we were home. The past two days, he's slept 75% of the time. I did the basic math at dinner tonight, and that means he's been sleeping an estimated 18 hours out of each 24-hour period. "Seems about right," I said. Seth smiled with little reply as he walked back upstairs to bed.

I trust Seth is sleeping so much because the trauma his body has experienced has worn him down. I trust Seth is sleeping so much because radiation makes you tired. I trust Seth is sleeping so much because the invisible emotional, mental, and spiritual toll cancer has on an individual has to be managed somehow. And I trust Seth is sleeping so much because it's helping him heal.

Since Seth was admitted to the hospital 10 days ago, I've had a number of dreams about children, swarms of children and my trip to the Dominican Republic with Compassion

International. Last night, my dreams went further back in time to the camera I purchased five months ago. In the dream, I was on location for a photo shoot at a hotel or building that was large with long hallways and a lot of elevators. I arrived at the shoot only to realize I'd forgotten my lenses, so I started heading back to find them, only to forget where I'd left them. It was an ugly cycle of forgetting and not knowing. I had the body of the camera with me, but I was getting distracted by all the children, and all I really wanted to do was take pictures. But I couldn't because I didn't have my lenses.

I trust I'm dreaming so much about the Dominican and children because I haven't had an opportunity to fully process the trip. I trust I'm dreaming about my trip to the Dominican and children because part of me wants a do-over. As in, bring me back to the morning of January 8, 2015, and let me do the whole month over again, but this time, take away the eye cancer part of it. I trust I'm dreaming about photography because my brain is stuck in September when I bought the camera. I haven't had a chance to process all the old things with all the new things. And the lenses? Well, I'm not sure I have clear sight of anything right now. I'm ready to photograph and experience this new life, but I can't quite get my bearings. I still need those lenses. I trust my dreams are helping me process all of this.

Since we returned home four days and eight hours ago, I've been daydreaming a lot more than I would have ever imagined, especially given the circumstances of eye cancer, caregiving, and heavy unexpected responsibility for our home and our children. Yet, I've allowed my brain to go there, to places in the future, to spaces I've yet to see. I'm still experiencing some of that emptiness, that hollowness I wrote about two days after Seth's eye cancer diagnosis and the day I left for my trip to the Dominican Republic. But I'm beginning to wonder if that's part of what new normal will look like. What's next isn't easy. There's not a clear paved path, but it is good. In fact, I'm believing it's very, very good. I've sensed strongly for a couple weeks now that I need to go back and weave a few more threads together from the past three years. I know exactly which threads need to be woven. It's just a matter of sitting down, doing it, and waiting patiently to discern what's next.

I trust I'm daydreaming so much because I'm clinging to hope for a better future. I trust I'm daydreaming so much because God wants me to believe He has a plan for my life. I trust I'm daydreaming so much because right now, I'm in a space where I'm living and acting in complete faith. Very little is known. And I'm a planner, organizer, and analyzer. So daydreaming is my way to bridge the unknowns with hope for a bright future. I trust I'm daydreaming so much because when it's time to move on to some semblance of new normal, I'll have even more direction and clarity about what's next. There will be trouble. But it will be good, as promised. God will heal. All things will be made new. And we'll continue resting in peace knowing there's hope. For tomorrow is a new day.

12

WHAT TRUE LOVE IS

February 13, 2015

It's been five weeks and a day since doctors told my husband
he has eye cancer. A lot has happened in one short month. In
fact, I told you two days ago that I wanted a do-over.
Let me do this month all over again.
Let me try again, God.
Can't we get it right this time?
But time machines don't exist. We can't press rewind on
life. We can't go back and change the course of history. And
we can't blame God for what He's allowed. There isn't a magic
formula for going back and erasing all the things we'd rather
not have experienced in life.

But we can embrace the mystery. We can trust, hope, and
believe that good can and will come from anything. We can
relive moments and see beauty in all things. We can choose to
live what we love, and love what we live.

I've learned so much about love on this journey
through eye cancer.

Tomorrow is Valentine's Day, and my husband is still
upstairs in bed resting from last week's radiation and

hospitalization. Tomorrow is Valentine's Day, and he still has to wear an eye patch and shield whenever he sleeps (which is still most of the time). Tomorrow is Valentine's Day, and my husband won't be able to pick up our baby girl and spin her around because she's too much weight for the stitches in his eye. Tomorrow is Valentine's Day, and we won't know if the tumor is shrinking until June. Tomorrow is Valentine's Day, and we won't be celebrating with flowers, a romantic rendezvous, or sexy lingerie.

Yes, tomorrow is Valentine's Day. We'll enjoy a special meal out as family. We'll send the kids away to their bedrooms. And we'll hunker down quiet on the couch. My husband with his eye patch, me with my fleece pajamas and fuzzy socks. We'll watch some romantic chick flick I chose from Redbox, and if we're lucky, we'll enjoy a glass of wine or champagne before we fall asleep way too early.

When we wake up the next morning, when we transition into the next two weeks of my husband working from home, we'll remember the love we've shared and the love we've been shown. And we'll know more than ever what true love is.

Love is patient.[1]

Love is sitting for hours on end in waiting rooms and hospital rooms. Love is remaining silent while you watch a loved one come out of anesthesia. Love is caring for kids when a loved one simply can't. Love is holding and lifting, getting wet and washing hair day after day when nothing about you says stylist. Love is understanding sleep patterns that never seem to end. Love is listening and forgiving when a loved one shouts out of fatigue for the poverty, sickness, and misunderstood dreams of this world.

Love is kind.

Love is delivering a meal to someone you've met two times. Love is leaving a gift and words of encouragement for someone you barely know. Love is gracing someone with your presence, caring for someone with a knock at the door. Love is a hug, a look, a call, a text expecting nothing in return.

It does not envy.

Love is being glad when your loved one's lavished on. Love is resting confidently when your loved one's receiving more meals, more gifts, more paid time off, and more attention than you. Love is chilling out when your loved one is getting a lot more sleep than you. Love is extending grace to yourself when your sick spouse is funnier and wittier than you are.

It does not boast, it is not proud.

Love is remaining humble at all times. Love is bowing down to meet the needs of others. Love is remembering that you, too, will need care someday. Love is knowing that anything could happen in an instant. Love is recognizing that healing, restoration, and reconciliation are not up to us, but God.

It does not dishonor others.

Love considers whether a picture would be appropriate to share on Facebook or not. Love does dishes. Love changes eye patches and dirty sheets. Love acts without recognition. Love keeps things private when it would be easier to shout out wrong-doings to the world. Love behaves bravely, boldly, and beautifully.

It is not self-seeking.

Love is staying home when you'd rather go out. Love is forgoing your night to make dinner for someone who really needs it. Love is going out of your way to buy someone a piece of cake. Love is allowing him to nap while you do everything else. Love is serving when you'd rather attend to your own agenda. Love is laughing when you'd rather cry.

It is not easily angered, it keeps no record of wrongs.

Love gives. Love forgives when it's really hard. Love

remembers but moves on anyway. Love sends emails, texts, messages, and cards. Love expects nothing in return. Love graces those who don't respond the way we'd like. Love never presumes or assumes. Love waits.

Love does not delight in evil but rejoices with the truth.

Love is brutally honest. *"You need to get out of bed now." "You have no idea what you're doing." "You need to take care of yourself."* Love goes above and beyond. *"You're brave."* Love is wise. *"You're going to make it through this."* And love rejoices long before it's justified. *"You will celebrate." "Spoiler alert: the tumor is shrinking."*

It always protects, always trusts, always hopes, always perseveres.

Love keeps on keeping on, even when it wants to give up. Love presses into hard things, ugly things, unseen things. Love delights in beautiful small things. And love knows it's never easy, but always worth it.

Love never fails.

Love keeps the end game in mind. Love is a legacy. Love is faith with skin. Love travels, draws near in all things, at all times.

And now these three remain: faith, hope, and love. But the greatest of these is love.

13

RANDOM UPDATES ON HEALTH AND HOME

February 16, 2015

When we decided to share our journey through eye cancer on my website, one of the promises I made to myself is that I would not compromise the integrity and tone of my writing for the sake of a hard-and-cold medical update. With the exception of one, maybe two or three posts, I've been able to maintain elements of beauty, inspiration, faith, and depth in this series. I've followed my heart and been organic about the 12 posts I've written prior to this one. But as I've reviewed everything that's happened, everything that is, and everything that's to come, I've realized we're in the midst of another transition. It's time for a simple post filled with lots of updates. So here goes, friends…a little bit of everything for those of you following the journey!

Random Update on Work

Our biggest update is that Seth returned to work today. Well, maybe the more accurate update is that he began working from home today and will continue working from home for the next two weeks. As of right now, he's scheduled to return to the office on Monday, March 2nd. All this back-to-work business means that Seth had to make an abrupt shift from sleeping 75% of the time to being awake most of the time (with the exception of a late afternoon nap, of course). It's only day one of working from home, but so far, he handled it well. I'm expecting an early bedtime tonight, though.

Random Update on The Eyes

Seth's had more continued eye pain and sensitivity than he expected. He's particularly sensitive to bright lights, bright spaces, and sometimes even modestly-lit spaces. One time, he got up from the living room couch and said his eye was bothering him because of the brightness. It was daytime, all the shades were closed, and no lights were on. As I type, he's leaving the room because he has "bright painful flashing" in his eyes from the overhead light. He's been using prescription eye drops 2x/day since the first day of hospitalization, and a special eye ointment several times a day. These help heal the eye and keep it protected, but he thinks they might also cause extra sensitivity. So for the first time, he did try some hours without the drops and ointment today. It seemed to help a bit.

Random Update on The Eye Patch and Shield

Per Dr. P's orders, Seth wears an eye patch and shield every time he sleeps. For two weeks, he's worn the eye patch and shield 75-95% of the day because that's how much he's been sleeping. But today with the transition to working from home, Seth's worn them much less. The eye patch and shield make sleep safer and more comfortable for him. He'll be wearing them until we return to the doctor in March.

Random Update on Lifting

Seth is not allowed to lift anything more than a half-gallon. When you start thinking about everything you lift, you realize how light a half gallon is. I've caught him cheating a couple times, for sure. But grace is the name of the game these days, so it's all good, right?

Random Update on Showering

At the recommendation of Dr. P, I'd been washing Seth's hair salon-style in the shower and sink since his hospitalization. He got tired of all the leaning back and lifting that accompanied salon-style, so he decided to move our shower head to its lowest setting and give it a whirl himself. Now he's showering as usual. It just takes a little longer trying to keep the water out of his eyes.

Random Update on Driving

Seth was directed to resume driving when he feels comfortable doing so. He's definitely tempted to try it, but I've been encouraging him to wait. Every time we've driven somewhere, he's complained of nausea, that it's way too bright, and he's had his eyes closed half the time. I'm pretty sure he isn't ready yet. I feel like a mom talking to her teenage son on this matter, but I'd rather be safe than sorry.

Random Update on Valentine's Day

Our family shared heart-shaped pizzas and a Disney Channel movie with a sweet neighbor girl Valentine's evening. We sent the kids to bed promptly at 8:45 p.m. Then we broke out a bottle of champagne and *The Fault in Our Stars*. Call me foggy and overly tired? I, of course, remembered the movie was about a young man and woman who were sick and madly in love. But I neglected to recall one small detail – the young man and woman had cancer. And oh yeah, the lead character's best buddy battled eye cancer and ended up blind. Guess I was watching with a different set of eyes when I saw that movie in the theater by myself last June. I hadn't remembered that part at all. Needless to say, we were both in tears.

Random Update on Getting Seth out of the House

This weekend, Seth wanted us to transition to a more "normal" Sunday. He planned for us to get up, get ready, go to church as a family, and have lunch at our favorite restaurant. He expected he'd resume his sleeping 75% of the day routine when we got home from church. But when Sunday morning came, he woke at the time we'd planned, but promptly fell into a deep sleep within a minute or two. He was sleeping so soundly, I knew there was NO way he was going to make it to church or lunch. So I let Seth and our oldest sleep, and I went to church and lunch with our girls. Tonight, same story with our son's basketball. Seth had hoped to resume some level of coaching, but when it came down to it, it was just too much, too soon.

Random Update on Getting Myself and the Kids out of the House

I've been feeling a little stir crazy. It's been cold and cloudy. I've spent 14 days straight in a hospital, hotel, and our house with the exception of runs to bring kids here, there, and everywhere. And I've been responsible for everything. With all that and President's Day off for the kids, I knew I desperately needed a change of pace. So today I took the kids to the Mall of America. We shopped and walked a bit. We ate at Panda Express. We made a visit to Coldstone Creamery (need I say more). And we shopped and walked some more. The kids were exceptionally well behaved. At lunch, our oldest said, "This is fun," and the youngest said, "This is good." They thanked me without prompting on the way home. It was a breath of fresh air.

Random Update on Getting Myself Some Help

May I remind you that I've been feeling a bit stir crazy? Yep. I've called in the big guns. My mom is coming later this week for one day to help with the kids. I'll do a little housework without interruption. I'll do a little private practice work so I can continue wrapping up those loose ends. I'll get out for a movie by myself and maybe an errand or two. And perhaps I'll breathe for a moment.

14

THE EMPTYING
AND FILLING OF A
CAREGIVER'S SOUL

February 23, 2015

February 7th, we returned home from a week's stay at the hospital. By February 15th, I was feeling fatigued and overwhelmed by the full-time responsibility for Seth, the kids, and everything at home.

But here's the thing…

I wasn't fully aware of my fatigue and need for a break until the possibility of a break was brought to my attention.

That afternoon of the 15th, I spoke with my mom on the phone. She told me she'd be willing to come and watch the kids for a day if I ever needed a break during this journey through eye cancer. I said, "Yeah. Okay. I'll let you know." When I got off the phone, I thought about it more and realized I should have just said yes on the spot. I texted her and told her yes. Please come. A day away will be great.

We agreed on the 19th. But my dad has a rare lung disease, never does great in the winter, and has been very sick with the flu the past couple of weeks. My mom needed to stay home to be with my dad until his new meds got into his system. So we moved my day away to the 20th.

I'm just going to say this, because it's true. When you're a mom it can be hard to take care of yourself.

I needed a break, time away from the kids and all the responsibility. In my case, my husband, Seth, was out of commission because of eye cancer. It was not an option for him to give me the break I needed. Most of the people we know have kids of their own to care for, and they work all week. While I'd had a couple offers to watch our kids, the truth was, I needed a big block of time away. I needed a whole day away. And the weekend wasn't an option because the kids had basketball and volleyball. It was just too much to ask a neighbor or really anyone else besides family.

My mom had been helping my sister reorganize her house, and my niece and nephew had been really sick, too. Add to that, my dad was not feeling well at all. To be completely honest, asking my mom to watch my kids so I could simply "get away" for the day felt incredibly selfish. My dad and sister need help more. Then there's this vague gnawing away, this ugly feeling that I'm adding to my mom's burden to care for everyone. And she never has or takes time for HERSELF. I don't want to be an added burden. I want to provide relief. Or at least, I just want to be benign.

But I needed relief. Yes, I needed relief.

So my mom came the night of the 19th and stayed at our house for nearly 24 hours.

I went to writing group.

I crossed paths with the mama of the first girl with Down syndrome I saw for speech-language therapy back in 2000. We hugged and caught up for a few minutes in Target.

I worked out, climbing stairs one after another.

Up. Up. Up.

Up. Up. Up.

Up. Up. Up.

We saw David, the man with Down syndrome we greet and high five on our way out of the gym every day. Earlier in the week, he'd pointed out a pin on his hat that said his birthday was Friday the 20th. So I brought him the picture Maisie and my mom colored in honor of his special day.

I went to Walgreens and printed pictures from the day I met our sponsored child, Meranyelis, in the Dominican Republic. Because of eye cancer, I was LONG overdue on mailing the pictures, and I didn't want to break my promise to Meranyelis to send them as soon as I could. When all those pictures popped up on the screen, I sensed the holiness of the day all over again. I picked up seven pictures I'd ordered from the day I met Charles last year in Haiti. Our sponsorship became official mid-December and I've sent a letter, but for multiple reasons, haven't had a chance to print and send pictures yet. I wrote two cards for the two kids, labeled the back of each picture with child name and number and sponsor name and number, and stuffed them in an envelope to Compassion International. Yes, I thought. This in itself is worth a day away.

I ate lunch by myself. Quietly. With no interruption. With nobody sharing or digging in my food.

I played on Twitter. Read some blog posts. Connected with a few of my favorite fellow writers.

I went to the fabric store to pick up some felt and elastic so I could make the Santa beard my oldest daughter was worrying about for choir the night prior.

I picked up a new box of eye patches and vitamins for my husband.

And I went to a movie of my choosing. *Birdman*.[1] Just the way I like it. Artsy, a little edgy, well-crafted and deep.

Before I headed home, I stopped at a party store and picked up a birthday card for the birthday party my son was heading to in less than an hour.

On the way home, they began calling me. My mom first, then my husband. Where are you? When will you be here?

Cooper needs to get to the birthday party. We need the card and the gift card. And you need to get home in time for dinner to be delivered. When are you coming?

Mom had offered to watch the kids for the day. And I needed a break, so I took her up on it.

It was worth it, so worth it. I was, and still am, incredibly grateful for my mom's offer and presence those 24 hours.

But my day away was coming to an end.

I opened the door to a happier place than I'd imagined on the car ride home. Everyone was fairly settled. Sure, they needed the card and gift card. Sure, he needed to get to his birthday party. Sure, my mom needed to get back home to my dad. Sure, dinner was going to be delivered in 35 minutes. Sure, things were fairly well.

But I was still needed. Back. Here in this place I called home.

I was empty. I was filled.

So goes the emptying and filling.

Love your neighbor as yourself.

15

A MEAL IS A QUIET
EXPRESSION OF LOVE

February 25, 2015

The goodness began on January 6th, two days before my husband was diagnosed, two days before we knew any of this was about to unfold.

I was scheduled to leave January 10th for a week-long trip to the Dominican Republic with Compassion International, so she left a lasagna and cookies at our doorstep for my husband and the kids to enjoy while I was away. She brought a card with warm well wishes for my trip. I was blown away to say the least. Who does this? Who brings joy and surprise blessings in the form of a meal? Who knows how to love like this? Who honors another's life and work without expecting anything in return? I knew now. I knew her name.

Little did I know, that was just the beginning.

Two days later, on January 8th, my husband was handed the diagnosis. Choroidal melanoma. Eye cancer. To tell the truth, it's all a bit blurry from there on out.

But here's what I know for sure.

Before we shared the news publicly, word spread like wildfire privately. Within 24-36 hours of Seth's diagnosis, my mom told me that she and my aunts were planning and preparing a week's worth of meals for my husband and three kids to enjoy while I was on the trip. On January 10th, the day I left for the Dominican, my aunt and uncle delivered several meals to our home. Before the meals arrived, I'm pretty sure Seth was a little hesitant to receive them. "I'm not on my deathbed," he said. "I can still cook. I don't want them going to all of that work just for me." But the truth is, my husband REALLY appreciated those meals. He and the kids ate them all week long while I was gone. He had enough stress with the new eye cancer diagnosis to process, full-time work, and three kids to tend. The ready-made meals were a true relief.

My parents' best friends transported me to and from the airport. When they picked me up at the end of my trip, Cyndy, my second mom, had a grocery bag full of food ready for us to bring home. They'd already done so much, and now a meal. I was blown away again, and we'd barely begun our journey. I'm sure Cyndy thought she'd provided enough for one meal, but it was enough for two. Truly, when you provide a meal, the love extends further than you know.

The generosity continued.

Warm muffins for our first trip to Mayo Clinic.

A big box of snacks and drinks for our week at the hospital.

Treats waiting when we got home.

Homemade chili, corn muffins, and fresh strawberries from a woman we'd met two, maybe three, four times.

A crock pot of spaghetti and meatballs, enough for three meals, with oranges and homemade cookies.

Chicken enchiladas, beans, rice, and brownies from a neighbor.

Ready-to-bake fajitas with chips, queso, and sweet popcorn snacks from one of my readers who attends our church.

A frozen meal from our church meals ministry.

Stuffed pasta shells, salad, and homemade apple crisp from our sister-in-law and brother-in-law.

Frozen lasagna, garlic bread, and ice cream delivered to our doorstep courtesy of an aunt three hours away.

A rotisserie chicken, fresh fruit plate, and Valentine's cupcakes from our daughter's friend's mom, handed through the car window as we left cheer practice.

Two heart-shaped ready-to-bake pizzas, root beer, and brownies from a family on our son's basketball team.

Homemade cookies from one of the boys on our son's baseball team.

Hot tortilla soup, chips, and sour cream at our doorstep.

Lasagna, garlic bread, and Seth's favorite, Reese's Peanut Butter Cups, from a friend who's near and dear.

Pot roast, mashed potatoes, carrots, and French silk pie transported two hours in a car to our table.

Homemade wild rice soup, cheesy bread, salad, and Italian soda delivered to our door from a sweet college friend we hadn't seen in far too long.

Yes, we have been blessed.

We have realized the power of a meal in time of need.

The meals that have been delivered, the meals that have sustained us these past six weeks have been nothing short of a miracle.

We are grateful.

And we will remember.

When you deliver a meal to someone in need, anyone in need, it is a quiet and powerful expression of love.

16

MOVING ON TO
NEW NORMAL

February 27, 2015

It's been a journey, friends. If you've followed along on my website, you've been with us through it all. We're not done with this eye cancer yet, but we're approaching another major milestone.

Seth hasn't been into the office since Friday, January 30th. On Monday, March 2nd, he'll return. He's been working from home for two weeks now and has made particularly great strides each of the past 12 days. It's hard for a wife to measure the health of her husband, but let me just say he fed the kids breakfast this morning and made oatmeal for me without prompting. That says a lot, don't you think?

I've asked Seth to share a guest post on Monday, his first day back in the office so you'll hear more from him soon. In the meantime, I wanted to share how I know we're ready to move on to what's next.

Halfway through the month, my daughter participated in a week-long cheer camp. Two weeks ago, all the girls on the cheer team were scheduled to perform at a boys' basketball game. Seth was still sleeping 75% of the time, so I had to haul all three kids out to the game by myself. Okay, so sports aren't necessarily my favorite thing in the world. Neither is hauling all three kids to any big event by myself. But I thought I was ready. I thought I could do this. I thought it might be fine. It was, in fact, fine. But it wasn't awesome. Granted, I did have a three-year-old with me and it was bedtime and it was late, but by the time halftime came and the girls finished their performance, I was READY. TO. GO. I didn't realize how drained I was until I was out at a major social event. My ability to socialize was ACCEPTABLE, but not ADMIRABLE. When I saw how social and talkative everyone else was, I realized how tired I was. When I saw how much fun everyone else was having, I realized how much we'd been through and how much we were still on the mend. I was tired. I wasn't really ready to go out yet. I wasn't ready to chat it up with anyone. I just wanted to see my daughter perform and go home. So I did just that. After our daughter performed, I picked up our stuff, let the two oldest stay with friends, brought the three-year-old home to bed, and went back a half hour later to pick up the oldest two. Half of a basketball game was all I could handle, and I never once felt guilty about leaving early.

Contrast that with last night. Our son had a band concert. Seth was awake, alert, and ready to go to the concert as if nothing could hold him back, as if he never had eye cancer, as if nothing had ever happened. We went as a family. My parents had decided, last minute, to come for the concert so we met them in the auditorium. I wasn't super social with everyone, but I never am. I did, however, feel MUCH more energetic than I had at the basketball game two weeks ago, and MUCH more ready to socialize when I did engage with people. Seth was reasonably energetic and chatted with a handful of people. He even kept an eye on our girls while my parents and I chatted with the superintendent. This was a MUCH different scenario than two weeks prior when Seth was in bed and I was out on my own, fatigued with three children. We left feeling good, not drained. And I'd dare to say, we left with a sense that this was quite "normal."

So this is how I know we're ready to move on to "new normal," whatever that is.

Today is Seth's last day working from home. He complained a bit this morning about his eyes being more sensitive to light than they had for a while. And he's still working in our bedroom with every blind drawn. But he took a lunch break and we went to McDonald's to celebrate, just like we did the first day he started working from home. We enjoyed chicken sandwiches, just like we did the first day he started working from home. Only this time, he enjoyed a shamrock shake.

17

CANCER-KILLING
OPTIMISM

March 2, 2015

*I've been writing about our journey through eye cancer for
several weeks now. It's been a ride, for sure. Writing has
been therapeutic for me, and informative and insightful
for those of you who have followed along. But I'll be honest. Something has been missing. I'm keenly aware that my
perspective as wife and caregiver is much different than
my husband's perspective as husband and patient. So last
week, I invited my husband to share a guest post. I wanted
to give him a place to process and express his experience
in narrative form – more than a quick, clever Facebook
update. I also wanted you to hear, firsthand, what this
adventure has been like for him. Without further ado, I
introduce you to my husband, Seth. Please extend a warm
welcome. It's his first time sharing on my website, and I
am oh so proud of the way he's handled it all.*

Today is my first day back to work. Today is my first chance to get back into a normal routine. Today is the start of a new phase in my eye cancer journey, but today is not the day for a full-on celebration.

Sometime later this year, we'll hear Dr. P pronounce the medium-sized tumor in my right eye shrinking. And a few months later, he'll confirm it again. Perhaps a year or two from now, he'll tell me that we're home free.

That day will be the real triumph. We'll take the day off, have a great dinner, and probably gorge on Dairy Queen. (Better yet, we'll take the day off from touring the sights of Jamaica, have a great dinner on the cruise ship, and probably gorge on Dairy Queen later in my new Ford F-150 Raptor.)

Today is not that day, but it is a milestone, and a damn positive one at that.

The year has not gone as planned. 2015 started well enough, but my January 8th annual optometry exam ended with an emergency appointment to fix a supposed detached retina the next day. And that appointment ended with a somber ophthalmologist telling me that I have a choroidal melanoma. His staff was already on the phone with the best doctor in the world for this type of cancer. A doctor who happens to be at the nearby Mayo Clinic.

I remember sitting in one of those awkward ophthalmology chairs and wondering how I was supposed to react to this news. The doctor had said "you have a rare form of eye cancer" like a mechanic would say "you've blown a head gasket" and an intonation reading "this is pretty serious, but we'll fix it."

So I responded accordingly, with optimism. I smiled, asked a few questions, and thanked him for his help. When the office manager, not a regular staff member, took care of me afterwards, bending over backwards to ensure I didn't leave there without an appointment at Mayo on the books, I sensed the seriousness of the situation, but also the confidence of the plan moving forward.

So that's the tone I took for my own. When I called my

wife, Amy, on the way out of the doctor's office, I gave her the news and a prognosis filled with positivity. Not only was that how the doctor gave it to me, but that is also how I live my life. Never is anything so bad that we can't trust God to deliver blessings in our life.

But people are different, and not everyone responds to bad news in the same way. Some people freaked out a bit, understandably. I'm sure Amy was knocked down by my call. And I know other folks were too. I hadn't posted anything on Facebook, but word spread fast across our extended family and within hours I was getting calls and texts. Within days we had received a trunk full of meals from Amy's aunts and uncles to get us through the next week, when Amy would be traveling to the Dominican Republic with Compassion International.

In fact, the support was staggering. Once we decided to be public with the news and capture every step on Amy's website, the response from our family, friends, and colleagues was amazing. You know how good it feels to have a birthday on Facebook? Brighten the glow a hundred-fold.

Over the course of the next few weeks, we received an overwhelming amount of love, prayer, and food from everyone dear in our lives. And when I was in the hospital, hearing that support was my favorite part of the day.

I never felt ill. I never had any symptoms beyond the very faint strobe lights in the lower right corner of my vision that triggered a mention to my doctor. And there were no drugs, no exercises, or no preventative measures to take between my first appointment in January and my surgery in February. So once I got used to having a cancer diagnosis – and getting used to it was surprisingly easy considering the positive prognosis – it was easy to settle into my life for a few weeks and forget about the whole thing.

My pre-surgery visit to Mayo threatened that calm. Three days of tests that included hours of taking pictures into my eyes using the equivalent of the sun to illuminate each shot was not fun. The official confirmation of my diagnosis in my right eye and the news that I even have a "weak spot" in my left was not a high point. But it was the doctor's aside – "Oh yeah, and you can't wear contacts again" – that caught me off-guard. Yes, I have eye cancer, but at least I had planned to look good while conquering it.

I'm still coming to grips with and planning my negotiation terms in the contact lens debate, but that's not what threatened all my positive energy at the Mayo. It was the realization that I was a young 41-year-old sitting in the waiting room near a stranger in much worse shape than me. A young dad staying at the same hotel as a woman who would be staying there for six weeks during her chemotherapy. A man who made eye contact with an old married couple, the husband wheeling around his bandaged wife. For the first time, I recognized my mortality.

It was the positivity of every single medical professional at Mayo, however, that ultimately kept my optimism strong. I met with dozens of grad students, nurses, fellows, and doctors in those three days, and not one of them looked at me with pity, not one of them gave off the end-of-life vibe, even while discussing the procedure for sewing a golden bottle cap filled with radioactive seeds onto my eyeball, the prospect for losing some vision, and the risk of spread. They counseled me in the friendly, urgent way a Disney World attendant helps a parent find a lost child in the "It's a Small World" ride: "This is serious, but we're going to fix it."

Two weeks later, I was in the hospital for two surgeries – one to sew on the bottle cap and one to take it off – and two uncomfortable sessions of coming-out-of-anesthesia nausea. There were plenty of reasons to be negative. My eyes scratched like gravel and we didn't hit on the right cocktail pain meds for many hours. The food was terrible, and I couldn't even watch TV because it was too bright. Nurses woke me up every four hours all night. And my wife and parents had to leave every evening at 8:00 p.m. when visiting hours ended.

But it's much easier to be positive. I had full days of rich conversation with my wife and parents, who drove up from their snowbird vacation in Florida. I enjoyed the quiet at night without kids because my mother-in-law graciously stepped in to manage the household. I connected with family members and friends on the phone and online that I hadn't talked to in ages. I took every nap I wanted in a surprisingly cozy bed and my favorite blanket from home. I sat up with a large, black coffee and listened with my eyes comfortably closed while my mom and my wife read to me the new well wishes as they were posted online.

Today, my eyes are nearly back to normal and get better every day. My early recovery was three weeks of eye patches, sunglasses in the house, and nearly full days of sleeping. But lately, my recovery has been cautious outings, working from home, and taking it easy.

Today is my first day back to work. Today is my first chance to get back into a normal routine. Today is the start of a new phase in my eye cancer journey, but today is just another day of tackling it with optimism.

— Seth

18

MAYO ROUND THREE AND SIGNING OFF FOR NOW

March 5, 2015

This morning, we made our way to Mayo Clinic for round three. It was time for Seth's one-month post-surgery appointment with Dr. P. We woke at 4:15 a.m. and headed down the road for his 7:30 a.m. appointment.

We arrived 25 minutes early, so Seth grabbed coffee across the street at Starbucks and I went straight downstairs to the piano, my favorite spot at Mayo by a landslide.

I sat down next to an elderly woman who'd placed a sign on top of the piano. I thought for a minute she might be performing, but she was a patient, and a regular at that. For 10 years, she's been coming to Mayo for treatment. Heck, Mayo's like a second home to her. The woman was feisty, brilliant, beautiful, and insightful. It was clear that whatever 10 years of health problems had ailed her had NO impact on her mind or her soul. She was amazing, a glimpse of who I'd like to be at 80-something.

We chatted briskly, like time was short, like we just needed to get down to the business of this piano we loved so dearly. She told me about the woman who comes to play every Monday and Thursday from 10:00 to noon. She plays by ear, by heart. She doesn't get paid a penny; she does it because she loves it. Doctors, nurses, patients, and caregivers pass in front of her, above her, all around her. What flows from her fingers is based solely on what she sees. If people's tone is somber, she plays accordingly. If people's tone is hopeful, she plays accordingly. She's witnessed moods transformed and hopelessness turned to hope as they pass her playing piano.

There's a small group of people who don't care for the piano music. They want to ban it. Get rid of it. Take that piano out of here. It's distracting us from our work. It's distracting for our patients. The sound travels too far. Move it somewhere else.

But people love it. It's healing. It's holy. There's no better place for it.

Move it over here.

Move it over there.

Forget it, man. The acoustics have been tested. The acoustics have been measured. THIS is the place for the piano.

The elderly woman and I ponder the WHY of it all. WHY this place? WHY here? WHY not here? WHY is this so perfect? The three-leveled open atrium? The curved walls? The walls mixed with open spaces for sound to travel and dissipate wherever it may? Who knows WHY, but God? This holy anointed piano is here because God wants it to be. Because He wants to heal HERE. That's WHY.

A princess donated the piano to Mayo, had it shipped after she'd been a patient. "It's worth $150,000," said the woman as we gazed at its grandeur. "Oh, I imagine," I said. "It's priceless."

We chatted some more, that woman and I. I loved her dearly. Such a treasure. Such strength. I could've sat there all day, but duty called. After all, I wasn't there to chat with an elderly woman, nor was I there to chat about a piano! Seth had arrived with his coffee and was gently prompting me from behind. "It's time to go, we have to go."

"Goodbye," I said to the elderly woman. "I hope we see you again. I hope we see you later."

As we walked to the elevators up to ophthalmology, I told Seth, "Twenty minutes in Mayo, and I already found an amazing story. I love this place."

"That kind of thing doesn't float my boat," he said.

"Oh, it totally floats mine," I responded.

We arrived upstairs and were called in within minutes.

Over the course of the next two hours, we saw a nurse, a doctor, and Dr. P.

As of this one-month post-op eye cancer follow-up, Seth had this to report to the doctors:

- He's continuing to see mild strobing lights in 3/4 of the periphery of his right eye. (Prior to surgery, the strobing was in 1/4 of the periphery.)

- His vision is "not as good as it used to be, but is acceptable."

- The vision in his right eye seems to have worsened as compared to before the surgeries, but when he has both eyes open and they're working together, it's just fine.

- He still needs Tylenol for headaches.

- He's using wetting drops for his eyes.

- No double vision.

- On the extreme periphery, his vision is not as "trustworthy" as before, but it doesn't seem to be a major problem.

The doctors checked his pupils to see if they're working together. They checked the pressure of Seth's eyes with some fancy device made by Medtronic. They did a quick examination of his sight. They asked a lot of questions and did a lot of "look up, look down, look right, look left."

As of this one-month post-op eye cancer follow-up, Dr. P

had this to report to Seth:

- Seth is on the upswvVing now in regard to his vision. His vision will continue getting better, probably for the next year and a half, then it typically gets worse after that.
- He has "perfect mobility!" (Dr. P was VERY happy about this.)
- Dr. P was fairly certain Seth would have double vision given the size of the tumor, so he was delighted to hear Seth hasn't had any issues.
- A few little stitches remained in the eye.
- Seth can do "anything [he] wants" in regard to exercise and lifting weights from here on out.
- Seth is free to see the optometrist for a new prescription, but will need shatter-resistant lenses in his new glasses.
- No eye ointment is needed after today.
- He should use Systane drops for dryness and eye irritation.
- Dr. P recommends prescription goggles for swimming.
- He should wear glasses all the time to protect his eyes, especially the good eye, even when getting ready in the morning. (Dr. P was most adamant about Seth wearing glasses. Yes, this has been a struggle as Seth shared in his guest post, but is something he'll continue working through.)

As Dr. P removed the stitches in Seth's eyes with tiny tweezers, I noticed faint classical music coming from the computer. I hadn't heard it before. Dr. P must have turned it on when he entered the room. The artist was busy with his craft. The art of eyes. The art of helping human beings SEE. The art of restoring VISION.

Dr. P called into an automated phone system and dictated a report in a flash. Amazing. Incredible. Brilliant. He shook our hands and smiled. "One-month check-up? GOOD!" he said as he walked out of the room.

Before we left, we made our next set of appointments for May 21st and 22nd when they'll look exhaustively at the tumor to see if it's begun shrinking. They'll draw blood, do an MRI, take an ultrasound and photographs of the eye, and Seth will see Dr. P again.

At lunch, Seth joked about how we'll make an overnight date of it. How we'll leave the kids at home with one of our parents. How we'll go out for a nice dinner, just the two of us, that first day back at Mayo, round four. How we'll stay in a quiet hotel and head back for more testing in the morning. Yes, that's my Seth. An eternal optimist. Always looking at the bright side of life. Even in the midst of eye cancer.

19

GETTING NEW GLASSES

March 25, 2015

Well, friends! I thought I was on sabbatical from eye cancer posts until late May, but no surprise, the story continues to unfold.

Two nights ago, Seth had his first visit with the optometrist since his surgeries and radiation for choroidal melanoma. The primary purpose of the appointment was a thorough post-op vision exam, but it was also a perfect time to look for new glasses. Seth's prescription was changing, he needed special polycarbonate lenses, and he hadn't bought a new pair of glasses for more than five years. If there's ever a reason to buy new glasses, it's now.

This whole wearing glasses full-time thing has been quite an adjustment for Seth. He loves contacts and hasn't worn glasses full-time since junior high. He's walked through a whole host of emotions, and has finally arrived at a place where he seems to have accepted the fact that he'll be wearing glasses from here on out. If he has to wear glasses, he's determined to wear them boldly and make a statement!

With that in mind, Seth really wanted to make sure I was

along for his optometrist appointment. He wanted my input and opinion on new glasses so we decided to bring the whole family. Crazy, I know. Three kids in a quiet optometry waiting room for TWO hours with hundreds of expensive glasses at reach? Yep. Crazy.

But honestly, it worked pretty well. We spent the first hour looking exhaustively at glasses. Seth tried on at least 30 pairs, narrowed those to 10, and ultimately narrowed again to six. The kids read, played apps on our phones, and took the opportunity to try on glasses for the first time!

Once Seth had the field narrowed to six, he quickly but thoroughly evaluated each pair for look and fit. Within minutes, he was down to two pairs, a black Jack Spade frame and a tortoise Gucci frame. The technician and I agreed, the Gucci frame was the one. But Seth was clearly drawn to the black Jack Spade frame. After a while of analyzing, overanalyzing, and taking photos to see how he looked in each frame, he finally decided to go up front to ask the office staff for their opinion. Hmmm. Surprise! They all agreed the tortoise Gucci frame was "the one!" Our technician asked another technician for her opinion. Tortoise Gucci it was! Out came Seth's optometrist to get him for the appointment. And her preference? The tortoise Gucci frame as well! At that point, everyone was laughing up a storm. Everyone (except Seth) had independently agreed that the tortoise Gucci frame looked best. Still, Seth wasn't so sure.

He put both frames on the table for later debate and went in for his appointment.

To our pleasant surprise, the doctor changed the prescription for his glasses "a bit, but not much." There was reportedly "even a little improvement in his left eye" (the non-cancerous eye). The doctor indicated that the left eye was likely compensating for the cancerous right eye. When corrected with his new prescription, he'll see 20/20, even in the right eye.

When Seth returned from the optometry appointment, he was fairly sure he'd had a change of heart. He decided on the tortoise Gucci frame. But he tried both pairs a few more times for size and style, and we analyzed more pictures. Because you know, we all want to look good in pictures.

There we were. The decision had been made. Tortoise Gucci it was.

But wait.

Seth had just purchased high-end sunglasses last summer. Now that he can't wear contacts anymore and we need to do everything we can to protect his eyes, we realized we were also going to need to buy a pair of prescription sunglasses. Fortunately, he'd tried on a few sunglasses early in the visit and had his sights on a pair that looked awesome right off the bat. He tried those on again and there wasn't much to debate. We'd found the sunglasses!

It was 7:00 p.m. We'd been there since 5:00 p.m. and the kids were getting antsy. The technician offered to send us a quote via email so we could move forward with the glasses and sunglasses purchases at our leisure.

We thanked everyone for their help and they wished Seth well. Off we went to Dairy Queen to pick up the Dilly Bars and cones we'd promised the kids for being patient for two hours in the waiting room.

Another day, another dollar, and two new pairs of glasses. Yes, we're grateful for sight.

The journey continues. Until next time, friends.

20

LIKE AND UNLIKE
ANY OTHER DAY

May 23, 2015

The day started like any other. Or maybe not so much.

Like any other day, we woke up early and got the two oldest ready for school.

Unlike any other day, they took a few pictures with daddy before getting on the bus.

Like any other day, Seth spent a bit of time on his phone, then a bit of time doing a little work.

Unlike any other day, I flew around the house, maintaining strict attention to what remained on the morning's to-do list.

Clean powder room. **Check.**

Spot clean disgusting blotches of food and gunk off the main level floors. **Check.**

Clean main level floors. **Check.**

Clean windows and glass in whole house. **Check.**

Put clean sheets on Cooper's bed (a.k.a. guest bed). **Check.**

Finish cleaning the kids' always-disgusting bathroom. **Check.**

Like any other day, I didn't feel adequate for this housekeeping job. I wasn't sure it would meet any *Good Housekeeping* stamp of approval. By the time we got to finish cleaning the kids' always-disgusting bathroom, I was exhausted and had to call for Seth's help. He changed the lightbulb over the kids' shower, set our three-year-old daughter up with supplies, and assigned her to clean the toilet. She did a decent job, but I pointed out the fact that she didn't get the base, that this would still be disgusting for any guest. "Ahhhh," Seth said. "Big deal," as he walked out of the room. Considering we were heading out for two days of appointments at Mayo soon, I had to agree. But I cleaned the toilet base anyway.

Unlike any other day, Grandpa and Grandma arrived promptly at 10:30 a.m. We showed them around, detailed the next two days of kids' events, and left the house by 11:10 a.m.

Like any other day, we stopped to get some gas.

Unlike any other day, Seth bought a bottle of Propel for lunch. Clear liquids only for four hours prior to his MRI. Twenty minutes later, we stopped for Jimmy John's. Real lunch to go, for me only.

Like any other day, we chatted the whole way there. Mostly about work. A little this, a little that.

Unlike any other day, we knew our way to the Damon Parking Ramp. No directions needed for this fourth trip in five months. We arrived perfectly on time for Seth's MRI. One minute early, in fact. Seth went straight in. I sat, breathed, listened to a webcast on Iraq, and hand-drafted a post inspired by the lady across the way.

Unlike any other day, we made our way to our hotel, checked in, and left within 15 minutes. We hadn't gone on a date in more than FIVE. MONTHS. Did we need a date night or what? After sharing a piece of bunny cake and peanut butter cheesecake at the Canadian Honker restaurant, we walked a half block down and spent the next hour and a half working in peace at a coffee shop. That was followed by dinner, a trip to wander the aisles of Aldi grocery store to explore, and a movie of Seth's choosing, *Mad Max*.[1]

Like any other day, I wasn't excited about a violent, non-stop action movie. But I'd left most of the day's decisions to him. After all, he's the one with eye cancer, not me.

Unlike any other day, we scored two 3D movie tickets for $17.00!

Like any other day, Seth LOVED the violent, non-stop action movie. I didn't love it so much, but did appreciate its artistic value, especially the drum and guitar playing dudes battling in the desert.

Unlike any other day, we went back to the hotel.

Like any other day, he went to bed before me.

Unlike any other day, we woke up in the morning, got ready, checked out of the hotel, and headed over for another round of adventures at Mayo.

Like any other day, Seth picked up coffee. I didn't.

Unlike any other day, Seth had several back-to-back appointments. Blood work. An eye examination. Eye photography. And an eye ultrasound.

Like any other day, I wrote when Seth was in each of his first four appointments. A twinge of guilt ran through me each time I broke out the computer, like I should be giving my husband 100% of my undivided attention. But those appointments were really just for him anyway. And he reassured me, "Go ahead and work on your writing. Stay here. There's no reason you need to come in with me."

Unlike any other day, we ended this fourth trip to Mayo with another visit to Seth's specialist, Dr. P. He popped his head in the room to say, "The systemic testing (MRI) came back okay," then left for further analysis of the morning's eye tests. We waited. Waited. And waited some more.

Unlike any other day, Dr. P had the news we'd been waiting for since Seth was diagnosed with eye cancer four months ago, the news we'd been waiting for since Seth went through week-long radiation and hospitalization three months ago, the news we'd been waiting for since he took a whole month off work recovering and recouping. Is the tumor shrinking? Or is it NOT?

Unlike any other day, Dr. P told us he sees "very little change in the SIZE of the tumor, but the internal reflectivity has increased substantially," which means that next time he sees us, it's likely things will look better in regard to the tumor size, even great. Dr. P showed us a bunch of graphs of this "internal reflectivity" and how it's changed since original testing back in January. Sure, the size of the tumor had changed very little. But it was hard to deny the difference in those graphs, the difference in the internal matters and workings of the tumor itself. Dr. P showed us another picture of the front part of the tumor. "It looks like it's retracting. That's better, too," he said. Had the tumor shrunk, we would have returned to Mayo in six months. Based on this visit's results, Dr. P recommended we return in three months. And he urged Seth to get the laser surgery he needs on his left eye.

Unlike any other day, we made our way down to Mayo's subway level. A lovely woman was playing "On Eagle's Wings"[2] on the piano. "I sang that song at my cousin Doug's funeral," Seth noted quietly. I leaned against a column and teared up. The news we'd just received was neutral at worst, from all indications trending positive, it seemed. I wasn't sad at all. Just filled with emotion, if that makes sense. In the comings and goings of wheelchairs and significantly sick people, children, and caregivers, the woman played on. On and on, she played. She played with her head up. She observed keenly, with every ounce of her heart and soul, as people passed. She let the Spirit run straight from her heart all the way through to her fingertips. *Yes, I knew it! Pure grace. Divine favor. This was the pianist the elderly woman told me about last time we were here!* The woman who plays every Thursday. The woman who plays by ear, by heart. The woman who doesn't get paid a penny, who plays according to the shifting tones of the room, who turns hopelessness to hope with simple, beautiful tunes.

Like any other day, I cried when I took it all in.

Like any other day, Seth asked why I was crying.

Like any other day, I said, "I just really love this." Yes, 24 hours have since passed. I know why I was crying. The work that pianist does at Mayo is EXACTLY the kind of work I want to do with my writing. She exemplifies my greatest life's dream. To bring pure beauty in the midst of significant pain.

Unlike any other day, we went back up to the Damon Parking Ramp, got in our car, and drove down and out of this fourth trip to Mayo.

Like any other day, we got another lunch to go, talked, drove, and hugged Seth's parents and our kids when we pulled in the driveway.

Like any other day. Unlike any other day.

21

THE LAST THANK YOU

June 3, 2015

Dear You:

Thank you. What more can I say?

Sure, we've crossed paths a few times. But truth be told, I don't know you all that well. We're mere strangers in the daily reality called life. Heck, you're nearly my neighbor, but for some reason, our paths primarily cross online, in this place, my website.

When you approached and hugged me at the gas station that day, the day before we left for a week of radiation in the hospital, my heart was blessed. Thank you for your hug. Thank you for your warm welcome. Thank you for your sweet smile. Thank you for taking time to stop and see how things were going. Thank you for asking how I was handling it all. Thank you for being you, right then and there at the gas pump.

And then that afternoon, when the kids discovered a bag and your card on our front doorstep? Oh, man. What a sweet surprise that was. What a blessing and delight that was. Who does that anymore? Who delivers goodness straight to someone's doorstep without seeking an ounce of recognition?

Your words. That card. I've read it many times already. It's stored in my Bible to remind me that people do care, that people do love, that people do understand the quiet power of words, prayer, empathy, and sympathy in times of need. I love how you wrote it all out, all your thoughts, all your feelings, all your questioning and wondering, all your wishing and praying for me and our family as we faced my husband's eye cancer treatment. Thank you. Thank you for your words.

And that necklace, that powerful display of faith and beauty? Simultaneously broken and beautiful? That's what life's all about, isn't it? Broken and beautiful. We're shards of glass, our innermost places filled with painful experiences, haunting memories, things we wish never happened at all. But those broken pieces create us, form us, make us into better, more compassionate people. We are broken. And we are beautiful. God intended it that way. So we humble ourselves. We surrender, trust, and believe that His desire is to work all things together for our good.

That second surgery, the one where the gold bottle cap plaque filled with radiation was removed from my husband's eye? I wore the necklace that day. I knew I needed the extra strength. For the unknown. For what was yet to come. For peace and comfort knowing I was broken, that my husband's eye was broken, but our lives were still oh so beautiful.

"In surrender, God can use our burdens as an avenue for His grace."

Surrender. Oh yes, girl. You got it. I have learned to surrender. I am not in control of life. I do not have the power to heal my husband's eye cancer, nor do I have the might to fabricate and maintain any sort of perfect life. The weight of the world is not on my shoulders. But surrender. Yes. Surrender. When we surrender, God steps in. Grace abounds. We need not work ourselves to death. We need not worry ourselves to death. We need not fear the worst possible outcome. We need to trust, hand it over to a higher authority. Surrender. Yes. Surrender.

You must know. This is the last thank you. I've been holding off on writing your thank you because words haven't seemed adequate. I've been holding off because I wanted to wait until the time seemed right. I've been holding off because my thanks seem small compared to the great gratitude I felt upon receiving your beautiful gift.

Thank you.

Thank you.

Thank you.

22

WAITING ON SHRINKING

August 15, 2015

I felt the weight of the day rush over me as we drove into the Damon parking lot for our fifth trip to Mayo Clinic in eight months. It's surprisingly easy to become accustomed to illness, to disease, to the crazy and hard things of life, but then there are moments that wake you to the reality at hand.

This is not ordinary. NOT. Ordinary.

We drove past our normal parking spot in Damon. Full today. All the way up to ninth floor for one open spot. We exited the vehicle quickly and made our way to the closest elevator.

As we turned the corner to wait for the elevator, I noticed a young amputee waiting with crutches. He was shaking a bit and holding some sort of therapeutic device I didn't recognize. All I could keep thinking was how handsome he was, and why in the world do bad things happen to good people? When we stepped in the elevator, I noticed the amputee's wedding ring. He moved to the side, gesturing kindly and graciously to others who entered. Hardship humbles a soul.

An older woman entered in front of me, then moved to

my side. She breathed deeply, loudly, audibly, wore a cardiac necklace, and leaned into her walker. "Ay ay," she whispered in-between audible breaths out loud. She breathed that way all the way down nine floors. I wanted to put my hand on her shoulder, ask if she was okay, if she needed help from this place to the next. I should have. But I didn't. We were running late for my husband's three-month check-up for eye cancer. Our day was filled with five appointments, and I didn't want to run later than we already were.

We made our way down the hall, past the metal sculpture I admired and the information desk I needed our first days here eight months ago, past the insightful, delightful piano player accompanied by two singers and a full house of patients and caregivers. I wanted to stop so desperately, to hear and see this holy glory, but we were late. So we pressed onward to the elevators.

All the rushing for nothing.

We checked in and proceeded to wait a half hour for the appointment for which we were late. Waiting gave us time to breathe again, to reflect on the day ahead. Seth sent a text to his parents. I kept thinking about the piano and how I needed to get down there with the healing and the holy. Then I half-woke to reality of a husband with eye cancer and broke out Amber Haines' *Wild in the Hollow*,[1] the book I've been trying to finish for two weeks. "Will you pray for me before I go in?" asked my husband unexpectedly. "Sure," I said, continuing to sit and stare blankly like an idiot. "Right now?" he asked. "Sure," I said, "right here in the waiting room?" as if BEFORE the appointment was some other time than NOW. So I prayed out loud right there in the waiting room. That we'd receive news that the tumor was shrinking this time.

Finally, he was called in for his first appointment. It was brief, 10 or 15 minutes tops.

We were directed to another waiting room where we waited some more.

Part way through the waiting, a couple in their late 40s

was escorted into the waiting room. I was trying to figure out which one was the patient, and nearly commented to Seth how handsome the couple was when her phone rang. "I don't feel like talking right now," she said. I intentionally stopped listening in on her conversation, but couldn't stop observing her body language. She was clearly distraught. Distressed. Very upset. And so was her husband. When she got off the phone, a staff member came and told them they'd have to wait longer for their appointment, that they needed to get some lunch, that they should check back in at a certain time. He sighed, head down. She was about to lose it. I nearly cried for the two of them across the room. Seth told me he'd heard more of the conversation. This was their first appointment. She'd just received the same diagnosis as Seth, choroidal melanoma.

By the time Seth got into his second appointment, we were 55 minutes behind schedule. But we made up for lost time with another quick appointment.

When Seth got out, he was worried. The photographs he saw of the medium-sized tumor in his eye didn't look different than any other visit. The tumor didn't look smaller. I reminded him he wasn't a technician. I reminded him he wasn't a doctor. I reminded him there's no need to worry. The prognosis is good. I reminded him that I'm hopeful and there's no reason to believe anything but good.

It was time for lunch. Two hours until his next appointment. So we made our way back to the atrium, back to the piano, my favorite, most holy place in all of Mayo. Jane and the singers had just finished performing. There they were, chatting and hugging, ready to part ways. Seth ran up to ninth floor to grab his prescription sunglasses out of the vehicle; his eyes were dilated and uncomfortable. I stayed with hopes that Jane would sit for one more tune at the piano. But no such luck.

We ate at a pizza place, the first quick serve restaurant we happened upon. Two pieces each. And a soda. We talked about our son who's about to get braces, who he was and who he's becoming. We talked about plans and dreams, things that may or may not happen in upcoming months. Life's a constant surrendering and releasing of what was, what is, and what's to come.

He wanted Dairy Queen for dessert. I wanted piano. So we stopped at Dairy Queen on the way back to the atrium.

We had another hour to wait. Funny, we were worried about not having enough time in-between appointments for lunch. Now we had more than enough.

The piano was still empty so we walked through the glass door to open-air seating. The temperature was perfect, and the garden was gorgeous. I took a seat and a few pictures of Seth to mark the moment. He seemed worried. Sad. Or maybe he was tired. He kept mentioning how he wished he could nap.

We rested. We read, although I more, as Seth's eyes were still fully dilated, making reading uncomfortable. And we recounted the remainder of the day's schedule.

It was 2:00 p.m. Time to head up for back-to-back ultrasound appointments. Seth checked in. I broke out *Wild in the Hollow* and read a couple paragraphs. Seth was called in for his appointment, so I immersed myself deeper in reading, then writing. Before I knew it, Seth was back in the waiting room. It was time for our long-awaited appointment with Dr. P.

We were called into the room at 2:50 p.m. Hallelujah! 10 minutes early.

One of Dr. P's fellows arrived promptly at 3:00 p.m. He clicked open all the records from the day. Clicked open all the records from our last appointment in May. Looked at a bunch of images. Scratched the back of his head. And made a few notes in the records.

"It looks like it's shrinking," he uttered calmly and confidently.

The fellow continued with an exam of Seth's right eye, the eye with the medium-sized tumor. "Look left. Look right. Up and left." He double checked the left eye too, the eye that required laser surgery two months ago. "The laser looks good," he said. "There are no other breaks or tears in the retina." After making a few additional notes in the records, he bid us farewell and let us know Dr. P would be in shortly.

Fifteen minutes later, Dr. P whisked in and out with med student, Ine, from Belgium. They were going to look through the eye photography and would be back soon.

I overheard Dr. P explain from a room down the hallway. "This is the top." His voice was muffled, so I stopped listening. But later in his explanation to the med student, his tone was as jovial as a world-renowned doctor could be.

As he walked down the hallway toward our room, he gestured "shrinking" with his hands. Perfect timing for his arrival in the exam room when he announced, "It's shrinking! You're just a slow shrinking kind of guy. It's shrinking. It's just shrinking slowly."

In January 2015, the tumor was 4.6 mm.

In May 2015, the tumor was 4.6 mm.

Today, the tumor is 4.03 mm.

A 12% reduction in the height of the tumor. "We're going in the right direction," said Dr. P.

Dr. P examined Seth's eye closer, like he's done every other visit. "Yep, you can see it's falling backwards, which is the direction we want." Then, in an unexpected turn of events, Dr. P called the fellow back into the room. He pulled up one photograph of Seth's eye from May, noted some things for the fellow, asked him to take a second look at Seth's eye, and wanted him to answer the question – "How has this part of the eye changed since May?" Dr. P pointed out this blood vessel. Then that vessel. And another one or two. Dr. P reminded the fellow not to be deceived or distracted by that vessel there, to focus in on this one, right HERE. How were they angled? How were they positioned? The fellow examined Seth's eye closer, responding, "Yes, I see."

"One sees what one knows," said Dr. P to the fellow.

It was brilliant.

I loved it.

So much wisdom in that little room.

So much wisdom for now.

And the future.

One sees what one knows.

Yes, Dr. P.

Yes.

Seth shook Dr. P's hand. Or maybe it was a high five.

I shook Dr. P's hand firmly. "Thank you very much." And the med student's hand, too. "It was a pleasure to meet you."

The nurse who's been in attendance at the end of every appointment we've had with Dr. P bid me farewell, "Have a great weekend, sweetie." I've noticed she's noticed me and appreciated the gesture.

The day was done.

Before we left, we stopped to make our next set of appointments, but they weren't booking that far out yet. Seth made a work call he'd needed to make all day. And I took a moment to release, breathe, and photograph what was below and above.

Downstairs, we walked a little more freely towards our car, a little more freely past the piano where a young woman played. Waiting on shrinking. Healing was beginning.

23

A TUMOR, A PIANO, PRINCESSES, AND WAITING

December 14, 2015

At this point, I can't remember how many times we've been to Mayo since Seth's diagnosis of choroidal melanoma 11 ½ months ago. Let's just say we've been to Mayo a lot in 2015, so much so it's almost like a second home. During our most recent visit, we received the good news that the tumor in Seth's eye shrunk 12% from its original measurement at the time of diagnosis in January 2015.

Monday, we woke well before the crack of dawn to get ready for another trip to Mayo. Seth had a long day of appointments ahead, eight to be exact.

We found before and after school childcare for our two oldest, but didn't have care for our youngest, so we decided to bring her with us. It's not ideal to bring a near four-year-old for a day of appointments, but if there's one thing I learned when she accompanied us for three days of appointments one year ago, it's that a preschooler is sure to be a blessing to patients, caregivers, and doctors alike. So we brought her.

The first of Seth's eight appointments was blood work. The line was CRAZY long, the longest we've seen at Mayo by a landslide. We had to wait a good 20 minutes in line before Seth checked in. Apparently, Christmas and blood work go hand in hand.

The waiting room was loaded with patients. Crazy full.

Lots of waiting going on in the waiting room. No surprises there, I guess.

Our daughter broke out some Peppermint Muddy Buddy's Chex Mix along with the new Disney Clip Princesses she received at her birthday party last weekend and played until her heart was content. She managed to entertain a few folks behind her, too.

Seth was called in for blood work. At that point, we were already 25 minutes late for his 9:00 a.m. CT scan, but we didn't bother with asking or calling ahead to let them know we were still coming. Mayo time typically runs late, but everything works itself out by the end of the day.

We waited until Seth was called in for his CT scan, then Maisie and I headed to subway level to hang by the piano in hopes of some music. No pianist had arrived, but we held out hope.

We got great seats, chairs two and three down from the piano bench. Charlie got one of the best two seats in the house, right next to the bench. Then there was the lady on the other side. Charlie and the other lady, they were regulars here. Much more regular than us. Charlie's been battling cancer all over his body for two years straight. He's lived in a local hotel since May. He'd become friends with the woman on the other side of the bench. I never learned her story, but she's been at Mayo quite a while, too. She leaves her camper here, in fact. At $60 for 2 months in spring and summer, it's way cheaper than a hotel.

I got to know Charlie.

Our daughter got to know Charlie.

"I like to be up here," he said.

I like to be down here.

Perhaps Charlie and I were a bit kindred.

"You think Jane's coming soon?" said Charlie.

"Yep, that's what we're hoping for," I replied without delay. Jane's the lead pianist here at Mayo. I've written about her before. I've seen her perform here more than once. There's something special about that woman, and since Seth gave us permission to wander during his CT appointment, I wanted a chance at seeing Jane again.

Before long, she arrived. Ah, yes. Jane and her beautiful, delightful, one-of-a-kind, patient and caregiver ministering, piano-playing gift.

"How Great Thou Art"[1] was first. Jane on piano. Then a male singer arrived, and they performed it all over again for an even larger crowd.

"That was incredible. Totally worth being here for that," proclaimed Charlie. I agreed. Totally agreed.

A bunch of Christmas tunes.

"Happy Birthday"[2] and "The Itsy Bitsy Spider"[3] for our daughter.

"The Marine's Hymn"[4] for a veteran on the other side.

"Somewhere Over the Rainbow"[5] with an impromptu solo from the elderly woman on second floor.

Wow. Just wow.

And then there was Jane, always Jane and her wandering eyes. Scanning patients, caregivers, doctors, and passers-by to perceive their mood, the tunes that would lift their spirits and meet their needs here and now.

I watched Jane watch them. I watched them. Then I watched Jane watch them again. What can I learn from this wise woman? Jane possesses the most amazing gift, and I've had the pleasure of witnessing her using it again and again. Ministering to a revolving audience is profoundly holy, profoundly miraculous. This is a gift worth cultivating. I get this, admire this, and could totally nurture this kind of art.

After a long while of listening, Seth texted he was done

and appeared in the atrium. I invited him to sit and listen. We had more than two hours before his afternoon of six appointments.

Our daughter made friends with Stephen, another Mayo pianist who sat at my side and played pretty princesses with our daughter. By the time Seth arrived, our daughter had made herself comfortable on the ground and invited Daddy to join her play.

They played.

We listened to Jane.

Daddy grew weary of princesses just in time for a little patient with sparkly, red shoes to approach and show interest. Her mama prompted her with the right words to say to initiate play. Little red-shoed girl wasn't sure about the princesses, but she knew one thing. They were worth a stop to play.

A woman arrived to sing, Stephen joined for a duet, and Jane played on.

Before long, it was time for the little girl to go.

An elderly couple was our cue to go. They needed seats and we needed lunch.

Cafeteria food sufficed before a walk to the other side of Mayo for more waiting.

A concert! Who knew? We were looking for quiet but instead found a crowd, cameras, and Christmas carols. We listened. And our daughter made fast friends with a grandma and grandpa to my left. Wouldn't you know, those princesses came in mighty handy. "Grandma" invited our daughter closer, asking to see Cinderella, Rapunzel and Ariel. I do have to admit that when "Grandma and Grandpa" left, the man down the way wasn't so interested in princess play.

Back to 7th floor for an afternoon of six back-to-back appointments. We decided there was no use for me to join Seth for appointments since we had our daughter, so he went back for his appointments and we continued waiting in the waiting room. The receptionist brought over a Santa coloring page, stickers, and crayons. Our daughter colored her page and the receptionist hung it high on the wall for all to see behind check in.

Seth returned. There was a LOT more waiting for his next appointment. He was called in at 2:50 p.m. for his 1:50 p.m. appointment.

Once again, our daughter broke out her princesses. She lined them up on the ground, made castles out of leftover sticker backs, had them hop over pop bottles, jump on sticker-back lily pads, and lined them on chairs and tables. Those princesses did just about everything, including entertaining our daughter, a patient's wife, an elderly couple, and an amputee nearby.

We waited, waited, and waited some more.

Our daughter played and played princesses 'till YouTube videos presented an opportunity for a blanket break.

3:26 p.m.

I'd lost my sense of purpose, but our daughter still claimed hers. She was back up, bringing joy to the receptionist, patients, and caregivers.

3:46 p.m.

Still waiting. The receptionist left. Our daughter was now hot and bored. We changed her into short sleeves. "Where's dad?" she asked.

3:48 p.m.

Received a text from Seth. He was done with eye photography and waiting for ultrasound examinations. The waiting room had cleared notably at this point.

4:13 p.m.

Still waiting. In three-year-old boredom, we'd moved to the other side of the waiting room for a change of pace. Standing now.

4:20 p.m.

Still waiting. I caught our daughter jumping off a waiting room chair. We're wandering halls now.

4:30 p.m.

Still waiting. Camped in the hallway.

4:33 p.m.

Text from Seth. He was back in the waiting area and invited us to join him since it was quiet back there. We decided to take a chance and join him for his last and most important appointment with Dr. P.

4:43 p.m.

Finally in Dr. P's exam room.

This was the first time we'd ever brought a child into a visit with Dr. P. We weren't sure how it'd go, but it went swimmingly well.

Dr. P arrived. He got straight to business. "You're doing very well," he exclaimed. "The CT scan is clear. The tumor is shrinking." He gave Seth a hug and joked, "So what are you doing here?!"

Dr. P met our daughter and noticed her princesses promptly. To my surprise, he even gave Princess Ariel a whirl, picking her up, gliding her on the floor, and bringing her out to show a colleague in the hallway. He returned in a flash, handed the princess to her rightful owner, and got back to work.

Dr. P took a second look through the eye photography, and a first look through the ultrasounds.

Tumor was initially measured at 4.8 mm in January 2015.

Down to 4.1 – 4.3 mm in August 2015.

Tumor measuring 3.8 – 4.0 mm today, December 14, 2015.

A 20% reduction in tumor size since initial diagnosis nearly 11 months ago.

Dr. P was pleased. The tumor continues to shrink. He'll

see us again in eight months. Eight MONTHS. Wow. If that's not a sign of good news, I don't know what is.

Thanks, y'all, for following our journey. May health and peace be with you.

24

MY STORY

March 8, 2017

I woke at 5:07 a.m. on Friday, December 16, 2016. Within minutes of waking, I felt a tingle rush down my left arm. This wasn't your average my arm fell asleep kind of tingle. It was different. Significant.

For 2 ½ years, I'd been feeling tiny, barely perceptible, intermittent pains in my heart. And for months, I'd had several spells of unexplained dizziness when standing. Add to that three weeks of unusually elevated stress including two days of follow-up appointments at Mayo Clinic for Seth's eye cancer (which thankfully yielded positive results), returning home to grandma and three kids with head lice that would not go away for NINE days, Seth's birthday, a new website in development, my daughter's birthday and birthday party, one early Christmas with my side of the family at our house, and preparations for an early Christmas with Seth's side of the family. Add to that 12 years of significant stress, including my dad's layoff from his job two years before retirement; my sister's six years of significant addiction and mental health issues followed by two pregnancies and two children, one with a serious medical problem requiring surgery three days after birth; my brother's accident; my dad's heart attack; my dad's lung disease which lead to a lung transplant; my mother-in-law's heart attack; several years of chronic bleeding with multiple doctor visits and no answers; a vocation change for me; and lice not once, but THREE times, and I was beyond stressed.

I was certain, absolutely convinced that morning of December 16, 2016, that with the tingling down my arm, pains in my heart, unexplained dizziness, and ALL the stress both long-term and short-term, that I was having a heart attack.

I grabbed my phone from the nightstand, typed "symptoms of heart attack in women" into Google, and began reading the first article that popped up. No kidding. I didn't even make it half way through the article and my heart began beating so fast, so out of control, so out of my chest that I knew something was terribly wrong. Seth was sleeping, so I gave him a swift and hefty nudge.

"I need to go to the hospital. I don't feel well," I said with urgency.

"What?" he said as he pushed himself slightly up and out of sleeping position. "Are you serious?"

"Yes, I NEED to go to the hospital. Call 911 RIGHT NOW. I don't feel well at all!"

I wasn't sure Seth believed me. This was totally random. It was still 5:00 in the morning. I'd woken him from a deep slumber, asking him to call 911 and get me to the hospital.

"I'm not kidding! I'm going to DIE! Call. 911. NOW! I'm having a heart attack!" I yelled in a panic over my symptoms and Seth's disbelief and disobedience in not calling 911 the second I asked him to.

My eleven-year-old daughter rushed in our room after hearing me yell, "I'm going to die." I gave her a hug, held her hand tight alongside the bed, told her I loved her so much and that they need to call 911 right away.

At that point, I'm pretty sure Seth started to take the

situation seriously. He whipped his clothes on and called 911. As soon as he connected with 911, we got me down the stairs. I hugged all three kids as big as I could, told them I loved them SO much and to hang on until we could get a neighbor to come over to watch them, and made my way to the cold car. If I was, indeed, having a heart attack, and if, indeed, it was going to be fatal, I knew this was a beyond-traumatic way for my kids to see their mom one last time. In the panic of the moment, I did my best to reassure them of my love and give them one last memory of their mom holding their hand as she rushed to take care of her health. It was, indeed, a memory we will never forget.

After taking my heart rate and hearing my symptoms, 911 confirmed that they should send emergency services. An ambulance was on its way.

My husband helped me back in the house.

I lay flat on the living room couch with my blue snowflake pajamas and disheveled morning hair. My arm wasn't tingling anymore, but my heart rate was still unusually elevated, far beyond anything I'd ever felt working out faithfully for 11 years. I was dizzy, lightheaded, nauseous, and shaky. I felt weak and disconnected from my surroundings. I was going crazy, having a heart attack, or dying, or perhaps all three.

Before I knew it, my neighbor who's a firefighter was kneeling beside me. His wife was in the background gathering our kids and their basic belongings so they could hang at our neighbor's house before school.

An ambulance and two medics arrived. The stockings were hung by the chimney with care. The Christmas tree was decked to the nines with red ribbon, sparkly poinsettias, and Hallmark ornaments aplenty. And there I was on the couch having a heart attack…or not.

This was absolutely, without a doubt, the most humbling and humiliating experience of my life.

One male medic and one female medic rushed in the front door with their medical equipment. They asked about my symptoms and took my pulse and blood pressure. Still super high. Unusually elevated considering I was just lying on the couch. They listened and decided to take a quick EKG to see if any unusual heart activity could be detected.

Nothing. Nada. No unusual heart activity except my reported symptoms and extraordinarily high heart rate.

I KNOW myself. I KNOW my body. I KNEW something had happened and was terribly wrong.

I also happen to be a highly sensitive and intuitive individual.

I sensed pretty quickly that the male medic didn't believe me. He thought I was crazy, that I was making all of this up, that there was no heart attack happening here, that it was high time for them to get out of our house and let us take care of this in our own due time. Okay, perhaps I'm being overly sensitive, but everything I read from the male medic's body language was dismissive rather than supportive. I didn't need any sort of dismissive. Dismissiveness, whether subtle or outright, is not a way to bear the burden of anyone's story.

What did I have to lose in that moment? I'd already lost all sense of dignity. Heck, I was humbled prone on the couch.

"I know you don't believe me," I exclaimed as respectfully as possible to the male medic, "but I've been working out for 11 years and I know my body. I've never, ever experienced anything like this in my entire life. Something happened. Something is wrong."

"Let's see if you can get up and walk around a bit," said Jordan. I got up. Made a few slow laps around our kitchen island. "Have you experienced any stress lately?" inquired one of the medics. "Yes. Significant stress for many years." I shared the stress in a sentence or two, knowing full well that reality was more like a book or two.

Humbled and humiliated, I got back on the couch.

We decided, reluctantly, that the medics and ambulance would leave, that we would drive ourselves to the ER.

It hit me. I started crying as they looked at me one last

time and made their way out. Something significant happened. We called 911. I traumatized our kids. Our neighbors came over. An ambulance and two medics came to my house at a freaky early morning hour. And now they were all gone. It was just me and my husband. Something had happened to my body AND I was crazy all at the same time.

A half hour later, we found ourselves in the emergency room.

Four hours later, after physician interviews, a chest x-ray, another EKG, two enzyme tests used to detect a heart attack, and continuous blood pressure and heart rate monitoring showing my pulse was still totally out of control, it was determined that I had NOT had a heart attack, but a panic attack.

Yes, this was definitely the most humiliating experience of my entire life.

The only consolation was the emergency room doctor who said she could see in my eyes that it had all been too much, that I had been through a lot and my system crashed once and for all. She said she wouldn't have been surprised if my enzyme tests had come back positive considering my unusually high heart rate for all those hours; she's seen runners leak enzymes at those heart rates post-marathons. Yes, she assured me that my heart was, in fact, incredibly strong.

That was Friday.

I had another panic attack on Sunday and another on Monday. Monday, I made a doctor appointment for Friday. I'd read up on panic attacks and had no interest in this moving into the realm of panic disorder. Tuesday and Wednesday were okay, but my nerves were completely frayed that whole week. I could feel my heart beating all the time. I had to move quarter to half my normal pace just to fend off another attack. I did very little around the house and had to take breaks to sit or lie down throughout the day. Thursday, I had a panic attack. Friday, I had a panic attack in the morning and was not well when I went in for the doctor appointment. I scored top of the charts on the anxiety test and began a medication that's used to treat panic attacks that same day. Christmas Eve afternoon was terrible. I'm pretty sure I had panic attacks, one after another, all through Christmas Eve service. I only slept three hours overnight from Christmas Eve to Christmas Day because I was cycling through panic attacks all night long and was certain I was going to land in the hospital again. Yes, it was that bad.

Thank the Lord, my last panic attack was late Christmas morning on our way to the airport. We just happened to be heading to Orlando that afternoon for a four-day family vacation. God knew I would need to get away. The medication kicked in. I was able to enjoy the vacation and haven't had a panic attack since late Christmas morning.

From then on, I knew life had to change.

I knew I needed to take better care of myself if I was going to continue taking care of others.

I knew I needed to see the significance of my own story.

For the past two months, I've consulted with our neighbor who's a personal trainer. I've eaten more salads in the past two months than I had in a year. I increased my workouts from 2x/week to 3x/week and am lifting serious weights EVERY workout, which is a notable change from my mostly-cardio workouts. I've cut back significantly on sugar, fast food, and mindless late-night snacking, and I'm generally eating with much more intentionality. Every day, I log my nutrition on My Fitness Pal. I've lost seven pounds in eight weeks.

The last day I drank caffeinated beverages was December 15th, the day before my first panic attack. I started going to bed an hour earlier and have been sleeping much better. I've said no to some things and yes to new things. I'm trying to reach out when I'm in need of encouragement, community, and connection. Slowly, but surely, I'm allowing myself to dream again.

Something had to change. Praise God, things are changing. For He works all things together for those who love Him. He makes all things beautiful in their time. This is my story and I'm sticking to it.

25

THE GAP

Those of you who are highly attuned to dates and storylines might notice there's a gap between when I last mentioned Seth having follow-up appointments for eye cancer in December 2016 and when I next mention follow-up appointments in May 2018. Yes, that's a gap of one year and five months. Those of you who know the suggested scanning protocol for eye cancer might realize we missed one set of follow-up appointments that should have happened late in the summer of 2017.

Seth didn't have a biopsy at the time of his diagnosis in January 2015. We were given the option of having a biopsy, but the doctor didn't recommend it because of the location of the tumor. He said there was more risk than benefit, that it might cause more problems than it was worth. We trusted the doctor and didn't do our own research on the pros and cons of biopsies in the case of eye cancer. We opted out of a biopsy, not knowing how important it was until much further down the road. Had we done a biopsy, had we known that Seth's tumor had a high risk of metastasizing, we wouldn't have missed the set of follow-up appointments that should have happened late in the summer of 2017.

We were told there was a 25% chance that the tumor in Seth's eye would metastasize at some point down the road. Later, we found out that there is a 50% chance of eye cancer metastasizing. Had we known there was a 50% chance of metastasis instead of 25%, had we done the biopsy and known Seth's tumor had a high risk of metastasizing, we wouldn't have missed the set of follow-up appointments that should have happened late in the summer of 2017.

Two years after his eye cancer diagnosis, Seth became an unfortunate victim of a massive corporate reorganization. In other words, a single corporation laid Seth and approximately 600 other people off from their jobs at the same time. We realized very quickly that between Seth's position and pay, we'd need to open it up to a nationwide job search. He was laid off for a total of 9 ½ months. ALL 9 1/2 months fell within the one year five-month gap between Seth's eye cancer appointments. The nationwide job search was all-consuming. Seth was busy searching for jobs, applying for jobs, and completing job interviews. We were distracted. We were worried. We were consumed, once again, by something that happened to us instead of us choosing it. Had we known there was a 50% chance of metastasis instead of 25%, had we done the biopsy and known Seth's tumor had a high risk of metastasizing, had Seth not been laid off for 9 ½ months and distracted with a nationwide job search, we wouldn't have missed the set of follow-up appointments that should have happened late in the summer of 2017.

Having Seth laid off for 9 ½ months wasn't easy, so we were overjoyed when he was offered a perfect position in Seattle! Seth went ahead of us and started his new job. The kids and I stayed behind, sold our house in Minneapolis, and moved to Seattle two months later. Seth didn't have family health insurance for a good four to six weeks after starting his job, and the kids and I weren't even in Seattle until a month after the new health insurance became active. And then there was transition time for Seth to acclimate to his new job, for us to adjust to new schools, new people, places, and routines. We were all moved to Seattle by late December 2017, but it wasn't until March that I felt settled and started getting worried about the time that had passed since Seth's last eye cancer appointments, and then once I called, it took two more months to get in. Had we known there was a 50% chance of metastasis instead of 25%, had we done the biopsy and known Seth's tumor had a high risk of metastasizing, had Seth not been laid off for 9 ½ months and distracted with a nationwide job search, had we not experienced a massive cross-country move with three children under 18 years of age, we wouldn't have missed the set of follow-up appointments that should have happened late in the summer of 2017.

Seth and I discussed the gap too many times to count.

We asked ourselves "what if" questions more than anyone needs to know.

We wondered what would have happened if things had happened differently.

We wondered, in fact, what would have happened if even just ONE thing had happened differently during that gap.

No matter where the discussion led, no matter which way we looked at it, no matter how we answered those "what if" questions, we always circled back to the fact that God was guiding us. God was leading the way. God was providing for us in ways we had yet to see. His timing was perfect, and He was there even if we couldn't feel it, even if we couldn't see it, even if we didn't fully understand it. He had led us from one place, to another, and yet another. Even if things weren't perfect, there was no denying His grace and provision at every turn. We simply couldn't regret a thing. We couldn't deny His hand or His goodness. It was all grace, pure unmerited favor.

God guides us in the gaps. Be sure of this, my friend.

26

OUR NEXT ADVENTURE: METASTATIC UVEAL MELANOMA

June 16, 2018

When we stood in the sanctuary and said our vows to Pastor Darrell, Pastor Grandpa Selmer, and a church full of friends and relatives 20 years ago, we hadn't a clue about what better or worse, richer or poorer, or sickness and health would look like in real married life. That's amazing grace, for sure.

So when things started to get really hard in the summer of 2004, just six years into our marriage, we pressed into those vows and learned what it looks like to love in the midst of significant life trials. Trial after trial, we made it through. Fifteen years in, our marriage started showing signs of fatigue, but we kept pressing on, leaned into God and each other, and made it through.

Then came a major career change and three mission trips for me, an eye cancer diagnosis and treatment for Seth, and a lung transplant for my dad. We had lice in our household four times over the course of two years, and I landed in the ER due to a panic attack I thought was a heart attack. Seth was impacted by a massive corporate reorganization, which was followed by a great job offer and a cross-country move from Minneapolis to Seattle for our family of five.

But our next adventure was coming.

In early March 2018, I began contacting Mayo Clinic in Rochester, Minnesota, as Seth was due for his regular eye cancer follow-up appointments, and we needed to get them on the calendar ASAP.

After a long wait to get in, Seth found himself back at Mayo for three days of eye cancer follow-up appointments on May 30th, 31st, and June 1st, 2018. On May 30th, while Seth was sitting at Mayo with his parents, I was at our new house in the suburbs of Seattle for one last walk through with our realtor and the construction manager before we were scheduled to close and receive keys on June 4th.

That afternoon of May 30th, right after I'd completed the final walk through our new house, I received a call with good news and bad news from Seth. For better or for worse. For richer and poorer. In sickness and in health. Mayo's tests indicated that Seth's eye was doing well, but the CT scan revealed a lesion on his liver. They needed him to come back the next day for a MRI.

On June 4th, our new house closed, and we received keys. It should have been a joyous day, but it was filled with questions and unknowns.

On June 6th, while I was on my hands and knees sealing the grout in our new house, I received a call from Mayo. The MRI revealed 8-10 hemorrhagic lesions on Seth's liver, each approximately 1 cm in diameter. They suspected it could be metastasis of the choroidal melanoma diagnosed and treated 3 1/2 years ago. They needed a biopsy within one to two weeks, no later.

I literally felt sick.

I called Seth to share the news, and we brainstormed a game plan for how you're supposed to continue putting your all into a new job WHILE moving into a new house WHILE dealing with a significant medical concern WHILE being 1,700 miles away from friends, family, and the treatment center of choice. And then Seth reminded me in his normal but unusually optimistic tone that "this is just another adventure for us." I tried calling Seth's parents, but they were on the road, on their way from Minnesota to help us move into our new house in Seattle. I called my mom. Then I heard back from Seth's parents and shared the news with them.

While Seth's primary doctor at Mayo was out on vacation for a handful of days, there was debate as to whether we could get the biopsy done in Seattle or whether we would need to fly back to Mayo. But when Seth's doctor returned, he was adamant that the biopsy be done at Mayo since they've seen more of this than anyone else in the country. So by Friday morning, June 8th, our flights were booked to Minnesota for a biopsy and an appointment with medical oncology, "just in case."

That night, I frantically began packing loads of belongings from our two-bedroom townhome into my car. There was no way we were going to stay another night in that stuffy, dark, two-bedroom townhome. The lease was going to expire soon anyway. I was bound and determined that we'd start sleeping at our new house that night, even though we didn't have beds yet. We had the keys. That's all we needed. We shared the news with the kids, had a massive family crying session in the townhome, and drove over to the house for our first night's stay.

On Monday, June 11th, at 9:00 a.m., the moving truck and three movers arrived at our new house in the suburbs of Seattle. All of our belongings had been in storage for six months, as we'd lived minimally in a two-bedroom townhome while our house was being built. This was all part of the relocation package Seth received when he accepted the job in Seattle, but this was all feeling very odd and unsettling, not to mention incredibly difficult to know how to feel with a major medical concern looming in the background.

Monday we moved in. Tuesday we tried to get as much unpacked as we could. The living room, kitchen, and kids' rooms were first priority for functional, practical living. By Wednesday, June 13th, at 1:30 p.m., we were at the airport making our way to Mayo in Minnesota for Seth's biopsy.

Two days of me, Seth, and my mom at Mayo and a slew of changes and unknowns, we got in with a world-renowned medical oncologist who was supposed to have that Friday afternoon of June 15th off. We had an answer.

"The biopsy shows melanoma. We are dealing with a misbehaved tumor," said Dr. M. On one hand, "there's not a lot of trouble" in the liver, "but this could be the tip of the iceberg. Looks like we need to get busy," he said. "We don't have great treatments for this, but we have treatments that work."

Dr. M asked us what our plans were for this coming week. "Well, we were scheduled to fly home tomorrow (Saturday, June 16th), but we want to get moving on this ASAP, so we can stay if that's what you determine is best," I said. The truth was, I didn't want this to be happening in any way, shape, or form.

Dr. M got on it. While we were still sitting there, he placed orders for a MRI of the brain, more blood work, a full-body PET scan, another mid-week medical oncology appointment, and a first treatment at Mayo.

Dr. M gave us a brochure about Metastatic Uveal Melanoma and told us to read it at our leisure when we could process more effectively. He explained that this is a metastasis of the incredibly rare choroidal melanoma Seth had 3 1/2 years ago (diagnosed in 6 in 1 million people every year). He went on to describe three treatment options, then quickly concluded they've had the best success with immunotherapy, a new arm of cancer treatment in which they turn on the immune system to fight the cancer. Immunotherapy tries to break control and turn tables on the cancer. Seth is healthy and strong, so this is the best treatment option.

Treatment is every three weeks. Typically, they do two to

three rounds of treatment, then repeat imaging to determine the efficacy. For Seth, they will do two rounds of treatment and then repeat imaging.

Dr. M gave the scheduler a list of appointments that needed to be made ASAP. We returned to the waiting room and shared the updates with my mom. As we made our way back to central Minnesota where my parents live, we called Seth's parents who are in Seattle caring for our kids and provided them with updates. A few hours later, we made individual calls to our three children, sharing the news at a level that was developmentally appropriate for each one.

So here we are. In central Minnesota for two days with my parents, then back to Mayo in southern Minnesota for another week. We just moved into our new house in Seattle, Washington, five days ago. Our kids are there, 1,700 miles away, with my in-laws. And our 20th wedding anniversary is in eleven days. We will be at Mayo for tests and treatments at least five of the next eleven days leading up to our anniversary. What more can I say?

Right now, I don't claim to know anything about the world, how it works, and WHY things happen the way they happen. But if I had to say what it is that I know for sure, I'd say that we can make all the plans we want, but it is God who establishes and ordains our steps. I have no idea in heaven or on earth as to WHY God would allow this to happen after all we've been through the past 14 years. I am having a difficult time processing all the WHY God questions. I don't understand. This doesn't feel good, and it doesn't feel like it's coming from a God who is good. But I also spent the past 14 years developing a sturdy faith, so the Lord keeps spinning me in circles back to Him. I must trust, even when I can't see, even when I have no clue why this is happening.

And then I circle back to the vows.

For better, for worse.

For richer, for poorer.

In sickness and in health.

We hadn't a clue 20 years ago, but here we are. We're still kicking. The show must go on. This is what we vowed. This is what we promised. This is the truth.

So we ask for prayers to lift us up during this trial. For us and for our three children. We ask for the high-skilled, world-renowned doctors at Mayo and in Seattle. We ask for clarity as we journey this trial and determine each next-best step. We ask for our new home to become a place of refuge. We ask for new friends to come alongside us in Seattle. We ask for old friends and family to support us while we're here in Minnesota and when we return to Seattle. We ask for peace and positivity along the way. We ask for stomachaches to be eased, and tears to be shed and then wiped away with the softest of tissues. We ask for support in whatever way, shape, or form we need. Coming off of a 9 ½-month layoff, moving to a city that has a sky-high cost of living, then moving immediately into a major medical crisis is not easy on the finances. We ask for your friendship, your love, your care. We ask for your patience and understanding as we return calls, texts, and messages - or maybe we won't be able to return them at all. We ask that you bathe our marriage, our children, and our family in all the prayer you can muster. We ask that we come through this. We ask these things with deepest humility, with deepest regard for each human being who knows us and has seen us through 20 years of marriage.

If I could've written my own story, I wouldn't have written it this way.

But so begins our next adventure.

27

HOPE IS HOPE

June 21, 2018

Early yesterday morning, my friend, Tricia, drove 100 miles to meet me at Caribou Coffee across the street from Mayo's Saint Mary's Hospital. She hugged me with the longest hug I've had in a long time, we chatted, had some tears, and covered a whole wide range of topics in just one hour and thirty minutes. After I received a phone call from Mayo's business office reminding me that my husband's PET scan had been denied and that we needed to show up to the office and make a $7,500 payment before we had the procedure (which I am absolutely not going to do), Tricia handed me a necklace from which hung the tiniest of keys with the word HOPE on it. She chose a tiny key because she knows I don't wear a lot of necklaces and agreed it would be understated. But this morning as I type each uncertain word on the keyboard, I realize an even better reason for that tiny HOPE key necklace.

It's okay to have the tiniest bit of hope.

Whether it springs forth in abundance or remains a tiny seed nested amongst a host of worries, HOPE is HOPE.

I wish I was a super-happy, super-hopeful, happy-hopeful,

beyond-hopeful kind of person that sprung forth with "everything's going to be okay" language around every turn. Honestly, I've wished for that kind of personality, that kind of perspective, more than I'd care to admit. Christian and American culture has tried to convince me that it's totally in my power to decide how much hope, how much positivity I have about life's circumstances. Believe me, if I could turn on a switch and become super happy, super hopeful, happy hopeful, beyond hopeful at a moment's notice? I would.

But try as I may, God made me a certain way.

I'm the woman whose once-upon-a-time very serious career aspiration was to be a psychologist. I can listen to your stories and your burdens ALL DAY LONG. Bring me your tears, your pain, the things that have hurt you most. Bring me your impossible circumstances, your most unlikely of hopes, your NOT understanding why this or that happened or didn't happen. I can handle it all. It doesn't bother me that your life has been complicated, twisting, turning, filled with a whole bunch of things that were hard, don't make sense, or have tested your faith beyond measure. I believe, with all my heart, that there's purpose for our pain, that beauty and glory are waiting to shine through our stories. I believe that life's challenges are meant to strengthen us, fortify us, prepare us for an eternity of peace, hope, and the greatest of loves. I believe the best stories are those in which everything imaginable falls apart, but there's that flicker of hope, that light of hope, that tiniest key to life, HOPE.

When Seth and I walked through Door B yesterday, plopped on the exam room couch, and waited for the oncology doctor to arrive, I must admit that I had the tiniest bit of HOPE for the news we were about to receive. Seth had an MRI of the brain the afternoon before. To be honest, I was pretty worried. The only physical symptom Seth's had through all of this is headaches, bad headaches that have required him to take Tylenol almost every day for the past two months. He thought it was just stress, but now that we'd found out the melanoma had spread to his liver, they'd ordered the brain MRI and said they wouldn't be surprised if the metastatic liver lesions were "the tip of the iceberg." There was legitimate reason to fear.

So when Dr. M arrived and announced "the brain scan was clear," the tiniest bit of HOPE turned to a swelling, overwhelming HOPE. I didn't believe what I was hearing. I'd been worried, and so had Seth. This was one huge blessing, one very big relief. If nothing else good came from yesterday, this huge hit of HOPE overpowered everything.

Dr. M went on to describe immunotherapy treatment in more detail than we'd heard. The goal, in layman's terms, is to "turn on the immune system," rev it up, and "get all the good guys on this thing." Immunotherapy has proven to be effective on metastatic melanoma when the originating tumor is choroidal melanoma (eye cancer). With Seth's very rare version of melanoma, there is at least a 30-40% chance that immunotherapy will "shrink the tumors immediately." If immunotherapy isn't working the way they want it to, they will try other more conventional treatments. And then there was the list of potential side effects, questions we maybe didn't want to ask, treatment in Seattle three weeks from now, treatment and tests at Mayo in Minnesota six weeks from now, more treatments, and the reminder that this is "an unusual version of an unusual tumor."

HOPE.

Whether it's bursting and swelling out of us; whether it's super hopeful, happy hopeful or beyond hopeful; or whether it's the tiniest of hopes, HOPE is HOPE.

From here on out, I place no judgement on the amount of hope I have vs. the amount of hope Seth has vs. the amount of hope our kids have vs. the amount of hope Seth's parents have vs. the amount of hope my parents have vs. the amount of hope pastors have vs. the amount of hope our friends, family, and colleagues have.

HOPE is HOPE.

That is what I will embrace today. That is what I proclaim today. That is what feels right and seems right today.

HOPE is HOPE.

It doesn't really matter how much you have, how loudly you yell it from the streets, or how quietly you guard it in your heart.

HOPE is HOPE.

So I had hope, a swelling of hope, a bit more guarded and exhausted sort of hope, when we arrived for Seth's first immunotherapy treatment at Mayo Clinic yesterday afternoon. Nurse Bert was helpful, hopeful. She's been working in oncology for 35 years, many of those years alongside Dr. M. She reminded us that he is a world-renowned physician, sounded genuinely excited about how much HOPE immunotherapy has brought to the world of cancer, and had a fierce but friendly positivity to her that made you believe, yet again, that there was truly HOPE, even amidst these darkest of circumstances.

The nurse prepared Seth for the infusion. Bag one. Bag two.

The tiniest of hopes. A swelling of hope.

HOPE is HOPE.

28

FINDING HOME

July 12, 2018

I didn't realize how much care we'd taken to make our 10-year Minneapolis house a home until we moved into our new house in Seattle. 1,700 miles from home while staring a metastatic uveal melanoma diagnosis straight in the face is a surefire way to make everything feel a little out of whack.

Conversely, it wasn't until Seth and I were sitting across from each other at Pizza Ranch in Rochester, Minnesota, that I realized our mountainous suburb of Seattle had become more of a home than we'd realized.

This was and is the crux of it all.

This was and is the beautiful trust of it all.

Finding home isn't always as easy as it seems.

But there is always a sense that it must be true, it has to be true, it's where we're supposed to be.

If you've had the fortune of living in the same house for 20, 30, 40 years, count your blessings of stability and security. If you've moved, been displaced, found your way in a place far from everything you've ever known, you understand what I'm talking about.

From the moment the Minnesota Mayo doctor called me with MRI results indicating 8-10 lesions in Seth's liver while I was sealing grout at our new home in Seattle, there were questions about HOME. Should we get the biopsy done at Mayo where the original choroidal melanoma diagnosis was made 3 1/2 years ago, where my husband spent a week in the hospital with a gold plaque filled with radiation stitched to his eye, where liver lesions were found on CT and MRI scans 3 1/2 years later? Or should we get the biopsy done 1,700 miles away in Seattle, the place we now called home? Our choroidal melanoma doctor was adamant. We must get the liver biopsy done at Mayo. They are the best of the best. They've seen more of this incredibly rare form of melanoma than anyone on earth. So we had the biopsy at Mayo, we got the metastatic melanoma diagnosis at Mayo, we had an MRI of the brain at Mayo, and my husband had his first immunotherapy treatment at Mayo.

But questions of HOME lingered, even so.

The plan was to have that first immunotherapy treatment at Mayo, to come home and have the second immunotherapy treatment in Seattle three weeks later, then return to Mayo another three weeks later for a third treatment and more scans. After that? Well, we'd go from there.

So after our unplanned 10-day trip to Minnesota and Mayo Clinic, after we landed in Seattle, right after we got in the car to head back home, I made the call to Seattle Cancer Care Alliance so we could get an appointment set up for Seth.

Eleven days later, Seth and I were sitting in an office downtown Seattle, waiting to meet another new doctor. The journey had already been exhausting. Adding to the exhaustion was 2 1/2 hours and seven phone calls with insurance and Seattle Cancer Care Alliance the day before, and 45 minutes of me meeting with a financial rep from family services trying to figure out whether or not Seattle Cancer Care Alliance was in-network with our insurance. Thank GOD, all the work was worth our effort. The Alliance is IN-network, thanks to a special network of University Physicians we have access to as part of our insurance plan.

Finding home isn't always as easy as it seems.

A consultation with the Seattle doctor was required before Seth's second immunotherapy treatment could even be scheduled. The doctor had reviewed the case, but had us provide a full review anyway. Seth explained the side effects he'd experienced since his first immunotherapy treatment – full-body itching, low-grade joint aching, fatigue, nausea, and a bit of diarrhea setting in. Dr. V explained that with immunotherapy, the side effects are more unpredictable than traditional cancer treatments. He explained things to watch for down the pike and predicted that the worst of the side effects are still to come. Then there were what-next questions, what-if questions, and those dreaded questions about HOME. Dr. V from Seattle Cancer Care Alliance was going to call Dr. M from Mayo. There were questions and differences of opinion on what the best dosing should be, when would be best to run the next batch of scans, and what the next-best treatment options would be IF immunotherapy doesn't work. We explained that we'd like to keep both providers, Mayo AND Seattle Cancer Care Alliance. This wasn't a usual nor preferred practice for Seattle, but the doctor thought it could work.

Six days later and just two days from what was supposed to be Seth's second immunotherapy treatment in Seattle, I spent another four hours on the phone with insurance, Mayo Clinic, and Seattle Cancer Care Alliance trying to determine where oh where we'd be getting that treatment.

Finding home isn't always as easy as it seems.

We finally got clarity. After all of the questions and uncertainty, insurance was dictating that we needed to choose one place or the other for treatment. We couldn't go back and forth between Mayo Clinic in Minnesota and Seattle Cancer Care Alliance in Seattle as we'd hoped. If we wanted to receive any immunotherapy treatments at home in Seattle, we'd need to cancel the authorization of six immunotherapy treatments at Mayo and re-authorize treatment for Seattle. One place or the other. One home base or the other. Not both.

Time had run out. Everyone had done the best they could to support us and follow the case hour by hour, but the truth was, Seth needed his treatment in 48 hours, and we still didn't have clarity as to where it was going to happen. We needed to make a decision and fast. Treatment was scheduled for Seattle, but we didn't have insurance authorization. We had authorization for treatment at Mayo, but didn't have any appointments scheduled.

I spoke with a nurse at Seattle Cancer Care Alliance. From their perspective, it was clear that time had finally run out. We'd need to fly and get this treatment at Mayo in Minnesota. Then after that, if we wanted to get any immunotherapy treatments here, at our new home in Seattle, we'd need to cancel the Mayo treatment authorization, get treatment re-authorized for Seattle, and the doctors here would need to be in the driver's seat moving forward.

Finding home isn't always as easy as it seems. Or maybe it's more that HOME can be elusive because we'll never be truly home 'till we're in heaven.

Time was pressing on these questions of home. Where oh where would we call home for this treatment due in 48 hours? Where oh where would we call home for treatment of my husband's metastatic uveal melanoma? Where oh where would we call home?

When we circled back to reason and reality, the answers about HOME were undeniable.

1. Our house is in Seattle.

2. Seth's job is in Seattle, and our health insurance is through that job.

3. Our children are enrolled in school in Seattle.

4. We can't predict Seth's health moving forward. We need

to secure a local provider rather than flying to Minnesota every time he needs care.

Home is in Seattle now.
This is where we are.
Home is where you are.
Perhaps HOME is the presence of the Lord, wherever you are?
Here we are.
We are here.
Do you know where you are?
I called Mayo with an update and made them aware of our urgent situation. It took an afternoon, overnight, and into the next late-morning of researching on Mayo's end to get orders placed and appointments secured.

Seth booked his flight to Minnesota the afternoon of the 10th. At 4:30 a.m. on the 11th, I pulled out of our driveway and drove Seth to Seattle International Airport for a 6:30 a.m. flight to Minnesota. I stayed here at home with the kids and my family who's visiting from Minnesota. Seth was greeted by his brother, Jake, at the airport in Minnesota, who then drove him to Rochester for labs and an appointment with Dr. M at Mayo.

This is not our preferred course of action. We wanted to use both Mayo and Seattle Cancer Care Alliance for treatment and testing related to Seth's metastatic uveal melanoma. But Dr. M understood. They suspected we'd need to transfer care to Seattle. This is home now.

Dr. M has spoken with the head of the Seattle Cancer Care Alliance. There are still differences of opinion as to when follow-up scans should be run and what kind of follow-up scans should be run. There are still slight differences of opinion as to what the best contingency treatment options would be if immunotherapy doesn't work. Blood work revealed a level in the liver that was slightly elevated, slightly abnormal. Seth will need to return for more blood work next week to make sure it isn't on the rise. All of this will be done and decided at home, in Seattle.

For now, Seth is wrapping up his second immunotherapy treatment at Mayo Clinic in Minnesota, with brother, Jake, by his side. Tomorrow, I'll cancel the Mayo authorization for treatment, and we'll begin the process of re-authorizing immunotherapy with Seattle Cancer Care Alliance.

Finding home isn't always as easy as it seems.

Perhaps home is the presence of the Lord, the Abba Father's Spirit, wherever you are.

29

QUESTIONS OF LIFE AND DEATH

August 2, 2018

"How long will it be before you know if the immunotherapy is working?"

"Why are we taking family photos?"

"Have they told you what stage his metastatic uveal melanoma is?"

"How are YOU doing?"

"What is your treatment team's success rate?"

"How can we help?"

"Is most of the hardship with your husband's illness?"

"Has someone talked to you about alkaline water, non-hallucinatory cannabis oil, eliminating sugars, eliminating GMOs, essential oils, or Protandim supplements?"

When you're ill or caring for someone who's seriously ill, you get asked a LOT of questions. I can tell you with 100% certainty that most of the questions aren't nearly as easy to answer as you'd think. And as far as the questions you ask yourself? There are way more questions than answers.

The doctors can't say for sure when they'll know if immunotherapy is working. Maybe 12 weeks, maybe 24 weeks, somewhere in between? We're taking family photos because when somebody in your family is really sick, it's a good idea to take nice family photos because you want to make sure to have those pictures and memories in case something happens. Well, technically stage IV, but staging doesn't apply in quite the same way with metastatic uveal melanoma. The short answer is that I'm doing okay, hanging in there, not sure what to think or where this is going. The long answer is four pages in a journal don't describe how I'm doing. We haven't asked about our treatment team's success rate because metastatic uveal melanoma is so rare that we'll probably be part of the data set. How can you help? Be creative. Get personal. If you think of us, maybe it's a nudge to reach out. Texts or encouraging messages work great. Yes, technically the current hardship is mostly around my husband's illness, but there were too many bad things before this and it feels like there are a bazillion potential life implications because of this, so pretty much life feels like it's on the line right now. And yes, I've heard of that. No, I haven't heard of that. I'm not really sure what to do with any of that natural, organic, holistic stuff because the doctors told us it would be best to keep things pure so they can measure whether or not the immunotherapy treatment is working, and to not muddy the waters with alternative treatments or other things going into his body. I'm all for dietary changes because that makes total sense, but it's all a bit overwhelming, so for now, I'm hanging on tight and trying to keep all the medical stuff managed along with every household need, child need, and future-thinking need you could imagine.

(Is your head spinning? Mine is. Truth is, sometimes it's spun so much it's blank. Let's just say it's a mix between a blank brain and head spinning, somewhere in there.)

What do all these questions have in common? They're questions of life and death. We're facing a metastatic uveal melanoma diagnosis, so these questions are in our face, no questions barred. But if we're completely honest with ourselves, we are ALL on our way to death. It's just a matter of time. Will we live another day? Another week? Another month? A year? Five years? Forty-five years? Who knows? Only God.

One thing this journey has taught me is that we'd all better get to living, like NOW. Today is the day the Lord has made for you and for me. Today is the day to live, for none of us are promised one more tomorrow.

We can ask questions. We can attempt to answer. Heck, we can delay or dismiss real and hard questions about life and death. Or we can face the truth straight on. The fact that we're able to ask questions means we're alive. We're alive, people. So ask the questions. Ask as many as you wish. Ask away, my friend. Questions are awesome, good. But questions of life and death are often elusive. Who knows? Doctors are humans. Treatment isn't foolproof. We're all going to die some day.

So live. Yes, live. Ask questions. But then live. Take family photos. Take that tropical vacation. Get a massage. Give your mama a kiss. Tell your dad you love him. Tell your friend she's a gem. Bring a chocolate cake over to your neighbor. Do something wild and crazy. Dive deep waters. Skydive if you want to. Read that book. Write the book you can't get out of your head. Hug your kiddos and write a secret letter they can open when they turn 21. Take the grandkids for a week. Play your trombone. Drive a convertible, ride a wild horse across the countryside. Whatever it is, do it NOW. We are not promised one more day. Today is the day to live.

Most of you didn't come here to read my philosophical meanderings on life, did you? I bet you have questions like, "How were Seth's appointments today, Amy? How did treatment go? Did they give you any idea of what next steps will be?" Let me tell you, friend, then I'll get on to the business of living. Because my husband is lying in bed next to me receiving his third infusion of immunotherapy for an incredibly rare form of cancer called metastatic uveal melanoma. We aren't fortune tellers. We aren't God. We don't know what will happen in the future. We can't predict what our future will look like, and we can't give anyone concrete answers about pretty much anything at this point. But we CAN decide to live to the best of our human ability. Today we will live. Today we will enjoy each other. Today we will remember to reach out and touch one another. Today we will be present, here and now. Today we will not take for granted a single second. Because today is all we have.

So as for those questions y'all have. Here are some answers. These are the only answers we have for today.

Labs came back perfect.

We met with a nurse who explained, once again, how immunotherapy works, all the potential side effects, and what to look out for during the course of therapy. We met with a nurse practitioner for an unusually long period of time. When you have a serious diagnosis, they give you a ridiculous amount of time with doctors and nurse practitioners.

During the first two infusions of immunotherapy at Mayo Clinic, Seth received a higher dose of Yervoy and a lower dose of Opdivo. Here at Seattle Cancer Care Alliance, they dose differently. Starting today, on his third immunotherapy treatment, he is being given a lower dose of Yervoy and a higher dose of Opdivo. The goal in making this dosing change is to attempt to reduce toxicity which can cause very serious cumulative side effects. These differences in dosing philosophies prove that even doctors don't agree on answers. Although we are not 100% sold on the decision to change dosing, neither approach is "wrong," so we are going with what the doctors recommend here, which is lower doses of Yervoy and higher doses of Opdivo.

Tonight, Seth is receiving his third immunotherapy treatment with infusions of both Yervoy and Opdivo. He will receive one more Yervoy/Opdivo combo treatment three weeks from now, then after that, he will receive infusions of Opdivo only, to reduce the toxicity load that comes with combo infusions of Yervoy and Opdivo. Once he's on the Opdivo-only treatment, there are more questions. Infuse every two weeks at a dose of 240 mg? Or infuse every four weeks at a dose of 480 mg? It will be up to the doctors and us to decide what's best based on Seth's unique response to treatment. More questions to come.

Another scan will happen mid-September. If the lesions stay the same or shrink, that's good news. If they grow or spread, then treatment decisions will be made accordingly. It depends. More questions. If the growth is small (like somewhere in millimeters growth), then they might continue with immunotherapy. If the growth is more widespread, then they would probably say immunotherapy isn't working and try something else.

Side effects are being managed well with medication and over-the-counter meds.

We can ask questions. We can problem solve and try to fix all of life's biggest questions around the round table (or maybe a couch if you want to get comfy). That's good, healthy, and necessary. But for some questions, there just aren't concrete answers. For those questions, it's better to give them a rest. Just sit. Breathe. Be. And live.

30

THE POWER OF A QUESTION FOR A CAREGIVER

September 6, 2018

In my 42 years of living, I've had the fortune of knowing three people who are ridiculously good at asking questions. A high school friend, a college friend, and someone who's served as a mentor to me in recent adult years. Today, I'm summarizing a month of medical activity with a story about how one of those friends asked a perfectly-timed question on a perfectly-timed day.

When Seth finished his third immunotherapy treatment for metastatic uveal melanoma, started complaining about headaches, was visibly distressed, napped all afternoon, then texted "I don't feel well at all" after I'd been floating down the river with three thirteen-year-old girls for four hours, questions filled my mind as I sped home from Fall City Floating.

When I found him in bed with chills, nausea, body aches, a headache that had become terrible, and a fever of 103.2, fight or flight set in. I was fighting. Hard. Fighting to the bone for this man, this husband of mine. Here we go. Off to the ER, just as the doctor had suggested.

When they drew blood, sampled urine, ran an x-ray and cultures of blood, but there were no identified sources or reasons for the terrible headache, super high fever, or any of the other symptoms, I was confused. All of this for nothing? No reason? No cause? That can't be possible.

When they brought in not one doctor, but two, to give us the option of a spinal tap to see if this was viral meningitis or bacterial meningitis, I wasn't sure what to say. How would I know what was the best decision? Aren't you the professional here? Clearly this is serious, but if it was super serious, wouldn't you be telling me what needs to be done instead of asking me?

When we decided against the spinal tap, they gave him Tylenol, an even heavier pain reliever, nausea meds, IV fluids, monitored him for another hour or two, and confirmed he was a "reliable patient" with a caregiver to monitor him closely in the comfort of home, I wasn't so sure. I was nervous, didn't feel good that we didn't have answers, was hoping he would be okay, and hoping I would be the caregiver he needed.

So when we ended up in the ER for a second time in less than 48 hours because a bad-to-the-bones full-body rash developed after the first ER visit, he still had a fever, headache, body aches, chills, his face and lips were swollen, and they were thinking he needed a brain MRI, I was in full-on something-is-wrong mode.

When there was blood in his urine, his kidneys were showing signs of distress, they brought the head ER doc on board with the case, took a biopsy of the rash, and my husband was admitted to the hospital, I knew this was serious.

When the brain scan came back clear, showing no signs of metastasis to the brain, the fever was gone, and they put him on a 50 mg dose of Prednisone to reduce inflammation in the body, I was relieved. Our worst fears hadn't come true. It hadn't spread to the brain. Hallelujah. Some One was helping.

Somebody was helping. Something was helping.

When I went home to sleep for the night and came back to a loopy, pumped up, and talkative husband who hadn't slept all night because of Prednisone, I was taken aback. Who is this man? Are we really in the hospital? Did all of this just happen? How am I supposed to wrap my mind around all this information? The rash was still horrific. Head to toe, worst shoulders to knee, both front and back of his body. It had turned a darker purple and was visually alarming. They added a topical steroid and asked us to apply it twice a day.

When they narrowed the diagnosis to "drug-induced lichenoid" or "drug-induced Lupus," and told us they may or may not need to stop immunotherapy as a result of this severe drug reaction, I wasn't sure what to think. Another diagnosis? STOP immunotherapy? What does that all mean, and what does that mean for our future?

So when my best friend from college and her husband arrived at the hospital that morning, my husband was looped up, pumped up and oh-so talkative after being on steroids for 12 hours, I was so incredibly grateful and relieved. A familiar face. A safe space to talk and be. Therapy, a change of pace for me, my husband, all of us. We laughed, swapped stories, shared lessons and learnings on parenting teenage girls with iPhones, and talked work, health, and life.

When the first round of laughing and swapping stories was done, my friend and her husband went to the cafeteria to grab lunch. When they returned with salads, sandwiches, yogurt, and bananas, my college friend, the friend who also happens to be one of those three people who is ridiculously good at asking questions, got serious and directed a question straight at me, just for me, the caregiver.

There it was.

On the table.

Sitting there in the quiet space between us.

She and her husband on one side of the room.

Me and my husband in a hospital bed on the other side.

The question lingered a bit before I got around to answering.

"Good question," I responded, then I began an answer.

Here's the miracle and moral of the story. Within 10 minutes of my friend asking that one simple question, our conversation led to the heart of the matter. Within 10 minutes, the question she was insightful enough to wonder and brave enough to ask led to the deepest, most pressing question I'd had rumbling and tumbling around in my heart since my husband's metastatic uveal melanoma diagnosis two months prior. Her question led to the heart of the matter. And that, my friends, is the power of a good friend. It is also the perfectly-timed power of a question for a caregiver.

Do you have a good friend? A really good friend?

Do you have a friend who knows how to ask the very-best questions?

Do you know how to ask very-best questions?

Truth be told, I don't know if I'm awesome at asking questions. I can tell you this for sure, I strive to be someone who's awesome at asking questions. Because I know the power of a good question. It's more powerful than any statement, any argument, any logic or any matter. Questions are where it's at, folks.

Here's what I know from observing my three friends who are incredibly gifted at asking questions.

1. They are all incredibly good listeners. They listen to what is being said, but they also listen to what is not being said. They listen to the spaces between.

2. Their timing is impeccable. If you are a good listener, then naturally, the timing of your question will not only be perfect, but impeccable. Listen carefully. Follow someone's story. Join their journey. And you will see, there are questions that need to be asked, terrain that's waiting to be explored, questions that are yet to be answered. What you do with someone's story, how you listen, how you

respond is crucial. Don't just blab on and on. Sit. Listen. Wait. Watch. And your timing will be impeccable, too.

3. Their perfectly-timed questions open doors to truest matters of the heart. Good questions don't need to be complicated. They just need to be the right questions at the right time. If you ask a simple but good question at the right time, you are offering space for the other person to respond with authenticity. Ultimately, this offering of time and space will lead to beautiful places. I promise you.

4. They don't feel a need to fill space with more talking. They just ask the question, provide space for the answer, and then follow-up with conversation and more questions as they feel led. My friends, questions are not powerful unless we allow space for authentic answering. This seems obvious, but most people don't know how to wait and listen for answers. This requires time, patience, and self-sacrifice. But I promise you, if you ask a good question at the right time, it will reap rewards greater than you would've ever imagined.

5. They don't pretend to know it all. They don't pretend to have answers. They just sit with you as you answer their question. They listen. They take it in. They offer their divine presence. They don't promise roses and wine, peace or triumph. They don't suggest you change your attitude or find perfect peace in God's perfect plan. They ask, and then they listen. That is the mark of a true friend. That is the mark of a good question. It doesn't have a right or wrong answer. The answer is the answer. The answer will lead to more questions. The questions will lead to deeper relationships. And if things really line up, the questions and answers will lead you back to the heart of God, your creator.

So she sat with me, that friend. She sat with me in spirit from across the hospital room, and then after she asked that question, after we got to the heart of the matter, after I started crying because that was the question I'd been asking myself for two long months, she joined me and sat with me on a hospital chair made for one. Because that is the mark of a friend. That is the hallmark of a good question. That is the power of a perfectly-timed, perfectly-formulated question for a caregiver. You can't make this stuff up. You have to live in it. Be there in it with someone who's going through something tough, something unbearable. Just ask a question. And be there to hear the answer. It isn't a quick process by any means, but it's beautiful.

We've been through a lot in that month since the hospital visit. Tests came back positive for drug-induced Lupus. Immunotherapy has been put on hold; we had to skip the infusion that was scheduled for two weeks ago. Liver enzymes were up, down a bit, and are back up again and not coming down. Scans are scheduled for sooner rather than later. We've taken family pictures and are working with a lawyer on updating our wills. We enjoyed a late night of country music ballads on the porch, have a seaside adventure planned for our family of five, and thanks to the energizing miracle of Prednisone, my husband is successfully managing a crazy busy three weeks at work. Tomorrow we go in for scans. Who knows what tomorrow will bring. But I rest now, assured that I have people who know how to ask good questions, questions that get to the heart of the matter, questions that resonate with my caregiver's heart, questions that meet me in my uncertainty, and questions that remind me that people care, people understand, that people are here for me and want what's best for me.

May I strive to ask as many good questions as I've been asked. May that be my future. A future of asking questions that are perfectly timed, perfectly crafted, perfectly held in space and time. May this be your future as well. To ask as many good questions as you've been asked.

31

WHEN YOU NEED EXTRA
LAYERS OF SUPPORT

October 22, 2018

We were in our bedroom when the call came in from the doctor. The tumors in Seth's liver had grown by 20% in size. Where there were 8-10 lesions upon original diagnosis of metastatic uveal melanoma on June 15th, there were now 14 on September 7th. His liver enzymes were notably elevated, indicating injury or inflammation. We'd need to see a gastroenterologist to get the enzymes under control. And since the tumors had increased in size and quantity, the immunotherapy combination treatment of Yervoy/Opdivo was deemed to be ineffective. The next best treatment option was a clinical trial in Denver. The gastroenterologist told us it would likely take "a good two months before the liver enzymes [were] stable and [he'd be] off all meds" used to bring enzymes back to normal.

Today marks FOUR months ONE week since Seth's metastatic uveal melanoma diagnosis. TWO months TWENTY days since he received his last treatment for metastatic uveal melanoma. TWO months EIGHTEEN days since his first ER visit. TWO months SIXTEEN days since his second ER visit and hospital admission. ONE month FIFTEEN days since we found out the tumors were increasing in size and quantity. ONE month EIGHT days since we saw the gastroenterologist and began an intense pharmaceutical regimen to get the enzymes down so his liver would be ready for the next treatment, a clinical trial called IMCgp100. ONE week since we found out that the clinical trial will be Portland, Oregon, instead of Denver, Colorado. ONE week since they sped up steroid tapering to get things moving faster for us. NINE hours since my husband went in for labs to see where things stand today. TWO hours since my husband texted letting me know that his liver enzymes are both finally back within normal limits after being elevated for more than TWO months.

So much unknown. So much uncertainty. So much waiting.

So much patience, trust, and faith to get through these trying times.

Back in mid-July, I knew I was going to need extra layers of support to get through this experience. So while we were waiting for one of Seth's appointments at Seattle Cancer Care Alliance, I stopped by the family and patient resource center and grabbed every handout on caregiver and family support I could. They all led me to Cancer Pathways, a nonprofit dedicated to supporting patients and families dealing with a cancer diagnosis. I submitted an online application indicating interest and providing information about our family's situation, and soon heard back from Maddie, the social worker responsible for coordinating services for patients and families. By late July, Maddie and I were playing email and phone tag in an effort to connect and get me interviewed so we could find the most fitting caregiver support services.

Phone and email tag weren't cutting it. I knew I needed to find at least one extra layer of support, and sooner was better than later.

Mid-August, I joined a closed Facebook group for spouses of uveal melanoma and metastatic uveal melanoma patients. A couple weeks later, I joined another closed Facebook group for metastatic uveal melanoma patients and spouses of metastatic uveal melanoma patients. Since joining those groups, I've become Facebook friends with three young wives whose husbands had or have a diagnosis of metastatic uveal melanoma; all three of those wives have young children and understand the impact this diagnosis has on the family. First layer of support? CHECK.

In August, we met a couple at our church who have a son our son's age and who also happen to be building a house two doors down from us! Early September, I was seriously debating whether I should join a small group to get to know more women in our church, or whether we should join a married couples' small group. One week before sign up, I happened to grab a packet describing each small group. But the week passed, and I hadn't taken one look at it. I was on the verge of giving up on the idea of a small group. Time had run out. But I had that packet and a 10-minute drive to church. So I sat in the back seat and scanned through the group descriptions as quickly as possible. There it was. Staring back at me as if it was meant to be. The couple we'd met a month before, the couple who were going to be moving in just two doors down from us, were hosting a small group and they were open to new members. We signed up for their group and started attending the next day. The group has been a tremendous blessing and thick layer of extra support during this journey.

In August, I began researching counselors. I wasn't 100% sold on a counselor for myself, but I'd spoken with someone who lost his brother to cancer and he said he wished he'd begun counseling sooner, so I thought I should at least research. One referral led to another, and I found myself a private Christian counselor 15 minutes from our house. She didn't accept insurance, but specialized in cancer patients and family members of cancer patients and came well referred, so

I knew I'd found my person. She and I agreed to a 1x/month session, which is all I need, can handle, and can afford right now anyway. Our first session was excellent and provided an added layer of education and practical suggestions I can use during difficult times.

Things finally came together with the nonprofit, Cancer Pathways, in Seattle. Last month, I joined a support group for families who are facing a cancer diagnosis in the family. I was blessed to find myself in a group of six women, all young moms whose spouses had or have a cancer diagnosis. Two women in the group recently lost their husbands to cancer. Four of us have husbands with a cancer diagnosis. It was a six-week group and our last session was last week. A new group will resume in January after the holidays. In the meantime, I can tell you this. The layer of support provided by that group was deep and rich, a profound gift of connection and authenticity with women who understand what it's like to live with such great uncertainty.

Why share all of this? Why not stop after the medical update? Because one of my greatest hopes for sharing publicly is that my story will inform, influence, and inspire your story. My ultimate desire is for you to see the significance of your story. If we're going to see our stories as having significance, then it's crucial that we're honest about life. Serious life circumstances have serious implications for all parties involved. When serious life circumstances come crashing at your door, the likelihood is that you're going to need additional layers of support to get you through. In my case, I knew I was going to need more support to get through this. In fact, I told Maddie at Cancer Pathways when I originally contacted her three months ago that I was just looking for "more layers of support." What I didn't know then that I know now is that I needed several layers of support. I needed two closed Facebook groups, individual contact with moms whose husbands were or are facing the same diagnosis, a weekly small group through church, monthly individual Christian counseling, and a caregiver support group in order to feel like ALL the bases were truly covered and I was getting ALL the support I needed. It was a shocking realization, actually. To realize you need an extra FIVE layers of support is humbling.

Here's what you need to hear. *You might need MORE support than you realize to get through what you're going through.* Reach out. Talk to a family member, a friend. Gather a group. Send an email, a text. Make a phone call. Connect with a counselor. Connect online. Find a support group. Join a small group. Get help with meals, cleaning, and child care. Ask for a break. Breathe. Accept help when you get it, and don't be afraid to accept help that's offered repeatedly, from that same person, over and over again. They want to help you. Accept it. Do something different. Step out of your box. If something comes to mind that might be helpful, try it. You need support. It's okay to say you need an extra layer of support. It's okay to say you need extra LAYERS of support to get you through whatever you're going through. Peace be with you, my friend. Your story is important. Be blanketed in layers of love, care, and support.

32

CANCER IS CONSUMING, BUT WE ARE PRESSING ON

November 7, 2018

A six-hour ER visit, nausea, fatigue, dizziness, drowsiness, lightheadedness, sweating, gastrointestinal issues, abnormally high heart rate, unusual bumps on his hands, red spots scattering his back, a light rash emerging on his abdomen and sides, a knot in his stomach, heartburn and pressure in his chest, feelings of fullness and air in the abdomen, feeling unusually and painfully full when ingesting small amounts of food, ear pain, sore throat, mild cough, and two days with oxygen saturation rates as low as 91 and 92.

These are the numerous symptoms and side effects Seth has experienced over the course of the past eight days. His diagnosis? Metastatic uveal melanoma, an incredibly rare form of eye cancer that metastasized to his liver four and a half months ago.

Cancer is consuming, but we are pressing on.

He stayed home from work one day. Went in for two hours the next day, three hours the day after that. Managed a half day the following work day. Worked from home yesterday. Trying to work today. Work goes on. Life goes on.

Cancer is consuming, but we are pressing on.

They spent two months tapering from 100 to 7.5 mg Prednisone, brought it back to 15 for two days to combat the host of symptoms, then dropped it to 7.5 again. Tomorrow, he'll be back on 15 for two days, then they'll taper and hold at 10. That'll get us through the next six days, then we'll meet with a new doctor who'll have his own set of requirements for the clinical trial we'll be trying.

Cancer is consuming, but we are pressing on.

Two days ago, we went in for a CT scan and MRI of the abdomen. Yesterday, we went in for an MRI of the brain. Today, we went in to meet with the doctor.

Hallelujah, the brain, lungs, and other organs are still clear and cancer free. But all the liver tumors have grown. Whereas there were 14 tumors in the liver at the last MRI on September 7th, there are now 15 liver tumors. Whereas the largest tumor (aka "Segment 6") was 3.5 x 3.1 cm on September 7th, it's now 4.1 x 3.2 cm on November 5th. Whereas the second-largest tumor (aka "Segment 7") was 1.8 x 1.9 cm on September 7th, it's now 2.8 x 2.4 cm on November 5th. The rest are the size of grapes or cherry tomatoes. Mayo Clinic's website[1] tells me that a 3 cm tumor is the size of a strawberry and a 5 cm tumor is the size of a lime. So the biggest lesion is somewhere between a strawberry and a lime. Seems trite to compare a strawberry, lime, or cherry tomato to a tumor, but for some reason, that helps us comprehend.

Cancer is consuming, but we are pressing on.

Seth's first treatment, immunotherapy, was deemed ineffective, as the tumors increased in size and quantity during the time in which he was receiving those infusions. He had a severe reaction after the third infusion, which caused his liver enzymes to soar out of control. Unusually high liver enzymes were combated with high doses of Prednisone, which was followed by a slow Prednisone taper. Three months later, we finally have normal liver enzymes again and low enough Prednisone dosing to move on with the next-best treatment option, a clinical trial. In six days, we will drive to Portland where we're scheduled for an intake appointment with Dr. C who is in charge of the clinical trial, IMCgp100. We don't have a start date for treatment. We don't know a lot of details about the trial, in fact. But in six days, we have the intake and will hopefully know more.

Cancer is consuming, but we are pressing on.

Every day, for the past eight days, it has been difficult to predict what the day will bring. Will Seth feel well? Will he be dizzy, lightheaded? Will he be able to work in the office, at home, at all? Will he be sleepy and ill in the morning, afternoon, evening, or all three? Will I find him reclining on the comfy chair in our bedroom, taking a break from getting dressed in the morning? Will he be in bed with the door closed or on the couch with the TV on? It's hard to say what ANY day will bring, let alone any hour. We don't know. We are hoping for improvement. We are hoping for stability. We are hoping for some answers. They're telling us it could be a virus that came on at the same time as he was tapering on the Prednisone, that his adrenal glands have taken a hit with all the Prednisone and can't keep up with production. Oh, and did I mention, we are getting a referral to the dermatologist for the unusual assortment of bumps on Seth's hands and red spots on his back? The oncologist took pictures. He hasn't seen anything like it. He's going to email the photos to the dermatologist and try to get us scheduled sooner rather than later. Maybe the dermatologist will know from just looking at the pictures, but she'll probably want to see them for herself. Does anyone know what's going on?

Cancer is consuming, but we are pressing on.

Our former neighbor texted, asking for our address so she could send something. "I'm so sorry from the bottom of my heart that I haven't gotten something out to you yet—there are really no excuses and all I can say is we were so busy..." She then went on to describe everything that's been happening in their family the past five months. The craziness, the chaos, the unpredictability, the projects, the trying to get everything organized again.

I stared at her text, wondering if she felt guilty for living her life and not tending to us sooner. I could write a whole post begging you to live your normal, regular, boring, everyday life, but the truth is…

LIFE is consuming, but we are pressing on.

She went on to say she thinks of us "literally every day," that they "are praying for all of [us]…and sending [their] love." I responded intentionally with "thank you so much." That's all that needed to be said. Thank you so much for thinking of us. Thank you so much for your prayers, your love, your kindness in reaching out during our time of need.

LIFE is consuming, but we press on hour by hour, day by day, week by week, month by month, year by year.

None of us know where each hour, each day, each week, or month will bring us. None of us can predict where we'll be a year from now.

So live, press on your path courageously. Recognize the good AND the bad, the yin AND the yang, the excitement AND the discouragement, the projects AND the piles left undone, the ups AND the downs, the joy AND the sadness, the health AND the sickness. For we WILL have trouble, but take heart, dear one. There is a God, and He has overcome.

So wherever you are, be there. Press on. Live hard. Take your vacation. Work that job. Hug your kid. Go on an adventure. Lie in bed and feel like crap. Pray to God He'll restore your son's health. Cry to the song you played on repeat when you were at your lowest. Live the best life you can. Every day. For today. Good or bad. Good AND bad. No matter what. Whatever life looks like. Believe it's okay.

33

CELEBRATING CHRISTMAS IN THE MIDST OF CANCER

November 21, 2018

We were eager to get home after a day of doctor appointments, but when I'd last changed our bedsheets, my husband's pillow protector disappeared. Thanks to heavy night sweats caused by metastatic uveal melanoma, a nasty virus, and a bunch of meds, and a pillow case not staying on the way it was supposed to, we were in desperate need of a pillow protector. "We're stopping at Bed Bath & Beyond. You can stay in the car. I'll run in. I'm getting you a pillow protector."

My goal was to race in and out, grab a pillow protector and move along. But there, right in the entry of Bed Bath & Beyond, was a hard-to-miss Christmas display. I have to admit. It was early, perhaps not that long after Halloween. But I'd been thinking of Christmas. In the midst of all the significant medical stuff, I was ready to embrace every good thing that comes with Christmas, even if it was a little early. I stopped, touched some poinsettia placemats, picked up a snow globe, and wondered if a sparkly gold candle would work in the farmhouse hurricanes on our dining room table. Wandering the aisles, I took a moment to soak in some Christmas peace before I grabbed a two-pack of pillow protectors and got in line.

"Ridiculous, all this Christmas stuff out so early," grumbled the guy behind me. He was clearly NOT happy with Christmas before Thanksgiving. "Yeah, it's a little crazy," I said out of obligation, trying to be as benign and agreeable as possible. But the second I said it, I knew it was wrong. I knew I needed ALL the Christmas stuff this season. I could have made him aware. I could have been that quiet voice nudging him to ease up on his Grinch tendencies. You see, I needed a bit of Christmas hope that day. Even if it was before Thanksgiving. Even if it was a little early.

The next day, I walked straight to the back of the drug store, straight to the pharmacy, then got in line to pick up two prescription refills for Seth. The guy in front of me was complaining to the pharmacy technician. Well, let's just say they were complaining to each other. Grumbling loudly, without reserve. "I don't trust these people who have all their gifts bought and wrapped already. That's ridiculous. What's up with you that you have all that time to be thinking about Christmas right now? Perhaps you'd better use your energy on something else." On and on they went. Grumble, grumble. Whine, whine. I listened but stayed out of it completely. The tone was judgmental, narrow minded. I just couldn't play their game given the serious nature of Seth's medical situation. Whether someone wants to celebrate Christmas early OR late, or early AND late is none of anyone's business.

Fast forward to November 12th, a solid 10 days before Thanksgiving, and we're driving three hours to Portland for an intake visit with Dr. C, the lead investigator for the clinical trial Seth will be starting soon. Pretty early on in the drive, he decided to recline in the passenger seat. He rested his eyes and I found some smooth jazz. "This reminds me of music they'd play in the MRI room, doesn't it?" I joked.

Seth agreed, chuckling a bit. "This is good," he said. So we listened to smooth jazz. Light. Easy. Unremarkable. Non-threatening. When he fell asleep, I scanned the channels and found an all-Christmas station out of Portland. "Feliz Navidad,"[1]"Holly Jolly Christmas,"[2] and "Have Yourself a Merry Little Christmas"[3] played as I drove my sleeping hubby to his appointment.

Before long, we arrived. I took a few pictures to mark the occasion, our THIRD medical facility for treating Seth's rare form of cancer called metastatic uveal melanoma. First Mayo Clinic in Rochester, Minnesota. Then Seattle Cancer Care Alliance in Seattle, Washington. Now Providence Cancer Center in Portland, Oregon. Been there, done that. Only this time, the treatment is investigational. Various studies across the country have been using this drug in trials for 2 1/2 years, and they're hoping to have FDA-approval in approximately one year. Yes, this time treatment means we're in a research study, utilizing a treatment that's not FDA-approved. Yet it's an honor to help advance cutting-edge treatment options.

We got in quickly. The nurse who entered data and took Seth's vitals was lovely. Dr. C was brilliant and quirky. The more he talked, the more I loved him. I wouldn't want my husband and the father of my children in anyone else's hands; that's a huge compliment coming from me. I'm picky when it comes to doctors. I have high standards, I tell you. This doctor was superb, the best of the best. He knew his stuff and was geeky, quirky about it. Then we were introduced to Chris, head nurse for the IMCgp100 trial. We were told he'd be our point person. He was gentle and smooth, kind and caring, knowledgeable and practical, just the kind of point person you need when your single eye tumor metastasized into 15 liver tumors and the first treatment option didn't work. Lovely. Brilliant. Geeky. Quirky. Gentle. Smooth. Kind. Caring. Knowledgeable. Practical. Plus there was a cross by the Providence sign everywhere we went. Everything we needed. I knew this was where we were supposed to be. As odd as it sounds, it made me happy, content, feeling full that although this wasn't where we wanted to be, this was exactly where we needed to be.

We're talking science here, folks. We can't be ALL sappy and smooth sailing. Believe it or not, there was a ridiculous amount of information disseminated during our intake appointment.

The clinical trial is called IMCgp100, a Y-shaped antibody engineered with a custom function. One part of the Y sticks to the melanoma cell. The other part of the Y sticks to the T cells. It triggers the cell to activate and kill what it's attached to. If you're lucky enough to be among the 50% of people whose blood tests positive for HLA2, you qualify for this trial. Fortunately, two independent lab tests confirmed my hubby is indeed HLA2 positive. We are grateful because the doctor said this is currently "one of the most exciting options they have for metastatic uveal melanoma." Forty percent of patients get a benefit, which is defined as some sort of tumor shrinkage. An additional 10-15% of patients see stabilization of the tumors. No patients have seen the tumors completely disappear. Once treatment starts, he will have scans every eight weeks. As long as there is "clinical benefit" (defined as stable or shrinking), he can stay on the treatment. Treatment is weekly. The first three infusions require inpatient hospitalization. The fourth treatment may require hospitalization as well. Treatment continues UNTIL: 1) the patient experiences "unacceptable side effects," 2) the "cancer grows or spreads," or 3) the "study doctor decides that it is no longer beneficial for you to continue receiving the study drug."

Action steps included a 10-day Prednisone taper from 10 to 5 to 2.5 to zero, then holding at zero for an additional 14 days before treatment can begin. A dermatology appointment, biopsy, and possible treatment of the bumps on his hands and rash on his back, chest, and arms. And a two-day screening process at Portland Providence. Phew. Breathe deep, Amy. Given the requirements and minimum timelines, the week of

December 10th is the earliest treatment could begin. By then, it will have been more than four months without treatment. But we are on our way. We are doing our best. Treatment will begin again.

I felt a strange sense of peace as we exited the exam room and made our way to the parking ramp. My husband didn't seem nearly as thrilled. Perhaps it was the news that it would be another month before the new treatment could begin. Perhaps it was the reality that this is one of the most exciting new treatments available for patients with metastatic uveal melanoma, but there's only a 50-55% chance that the tumors will shrink or stabilize. Perhaps my husband was just tired and worn.

He reclined and slept much of the way home. I turned on Spotify and enjoyed classic and acoustic Christmas tunes as I drove my sleepy hubby home to Seattle.

"Christmas songs, huh?" he said when he woke. "It doesn't feel like Christmas at all."

"Oh, it totally does to me," I said and kept on driving all the way to Hobby Lobby where we bought sparkly-tan poinsettias and creamy-gold berries for the Christmas tree before heading home.

Pumpkins are still out on the steps. The Give Thanks plate my mom sent is prominently displayed on the corner of our kitchen island, and the cute felt turkey is resting peacefully on our end table. Tomorrow we'll enjoy Thanksgiving dinner with my husband's parents who flew in for a 10-day visit. Neighbors are coming over for pie and conversation. We'll enjoy turkey, gravy, and a ridiculous abundance of food a friend of a friend dropped off for us. We'll give thanks. We'll express our gratitude for today, for these precious moments in time. We'll enjoy Thanksgiving. Then come Friday, the pumpkins and turkeys are going away and we're celebrating Christmas. We'll celebrate Christmas every day we can. We'll celebrate when it's far too early, before it's time, when it's time, and yes, even after the hoopla's put away. We give thanks and we put our trust in the hope of Christmas. Jesus. Came as a baby. For us. Pure joy. Death is defeated. Glory be to God.

34

I DID NOT PLAN
ANY OF THIS

December 17, 2018

Twenty-two years ago, my boyfriend proposed to me on the banks of the Red River in Grand Forks, North Dakota. It was his 23rd birthday. I was 20, and half way through my third year of college. We dined at a local Italian restaurant, then made our way toward the river where we walked hand in hand as snowflakes dusted our rosy-before-the-battle cheeks. I had no clue a proposal was coming, most certainly NOT on his birthday. But as my hubby-to-be knelt on one knee, I knew the only answer was YES. Yes, I will wait patiently while we're separated by several states for a year and a half. Yes, I will obey my parents' wishes and wait until I finish college before I get married. Yes, I will be your wife.

My last year and a half of college was spent studying for a career in speech-language therapy and planning our wedding.

If any Tom, Dick, or Jane would've asked me what I planned for life and marriage before I walked down the aisle that blistering hot day of June 1998, I would've told them

I envisioned life back in Minnesota after two years of grad school in Indiana, two full-time careers with solid income, a house in the suburbs, two or four kids (definitely NOT three), and celebrating our 50th wedding anniversary surrounded by children and grandchildren, just like my hubby's grandparents, Selmer and Anita. The plan was pretty generic, I tell you. The only things I knew FOR SURE was that I was going to be a full-time working mom my entire adult life, and that I was going to be with my Superman hubby until a ripe old age, holding hands 'till death do us part.

I didn't plan for life to look different. I didn't plan for life to take so many twisty turns. I didn't plan for any of the dirty details between YES and 'till death do us part. But I said YES to the husband of my dreams, YES to better or worse, YES to richer and poorer, YES to sickness and health, YES to doing life together. YES to my Superman hubby who sang me a romantic Elvis tune at our reception. YES as we first danced to Natalie Cole and Nat King Cole's "Unforgettable."[1]

I didn't plan for two years of full-time grad school to be ridiculously stressful with classmates who were a lot smarter than me, but I made it through with a master's degree anyway. I didn't plan to do home visits my first job out of grad school, but visited homes for 14 1/2 years and learned what it looks like to be powerfully present in the midst of peoples' rawest, truest stories. I didn't plan for six years of my sister in rehabs, hospitals, and halfway houses as she battled significant addiction and mental health issues and attempted to take her life more than once, but those years formed and shaped me and my sister into who we are today. I didn't plan to be the sole birth partner for my sister's first and second babies, but I was, and can say today that I've had the privilege of being present for the birth of five human beings. I didn't plan to have three children, but our third is a joy and the only person on earth who can make me laugh without saying a thing. I didn't plan anything but a full-time career as a speech therapist, but realized a year and a half into mothering that the full-time working mom gig was NOT going to work for me, so now I say "been there done that" with one, two, three, four and five-day work weeks. I didn't plan to start dreaming about a writing career when I was three years into the career I went to grad school for, but God sets dreams in human hearts and He'll see them to completion however He sees fit. I did NOT plan to leave my 14 ½-year career, but three years of prayer, contemplation, and consultation with wise counsel drew me closer to my Creator and richer in faith.

I did NOT plan for my husband to be diagnosed with eye cancer three weeks after I left my career, did NOT plan for that diagnosis to come two days before I left on a week-long dream writing trip to Dominican with Compassion International, and did NOT plan to go on a mission trip to Kenya 10 months after that. I did NOT plan to walk snail's pace with my dad on oxygen, did NOT plan for him to need a lung transplant. Did NOT plan for my husband to get laid off, did NOT plan for the layoff to be so long, did NOT plan to uproot our family and make a move from Minneapolis to Seattle, did NOT plan to build instead of buy existing, did NOT plan for everything to be so expensive, did NOT plan to drive UBER for four months, did NOT plan that our social butterfly would take the longest to adjust, did NOT plan that cancer would come back, that my husband would be diagnosed with metastatic uveal melanoma just six months after our cross-country move, did NOT plan to switch treatment facilities from Minnesota to Washington to Oregon, did NOT plan that the first treatment wouldn't work, did NOT plan for my hubby to be enrolled in a clinical trial, did NOT plan to be asking questions and having conversations I did NOT plan to have at 42 and 45 years of age.

Nope. I did NOT plan ANY of that.

I didn't plan to be blessed by the piano player when we went for eye cancer appointments, didn't plan to be emptied and filled back up full on that trip to Dominican, didn't plan to fall in love with Kenya and desire so desperately to go back. I didn't plan for the miracle it was when my dad woke up from his lung transplant, didn't plan for the joy it's been to walk with him at a normal pace. Didn't plan to put our trust in God the way we had to when we didn't know WHERE we were going, WHEN we were going, or HOW we were going to get there. Didn't plan to see limitless possibilities in a city I'd never been to, but was going to move to. I didn't plan to find a house we hadn't seen in a neighborhood we didn't know about in a city we'd all but discounted as a second-tier choice. Didn't plan that UBER driving would help me see (once again) what I was really supposed to do with my life. Didn't plan I'd adore our kids' new friends, didn't plan to adore the mountains, didn't plan to adore our new city. I didn't plan that a guardian angel with a southern accent would gift us with chocolate pecan cakes during our journey through metastatic uveal melanoma, didn't plan on non-stop support from out-of-state friends and family, didn't plan to be blessed by amazing doctors and nurses when we thought we'd lost the best ones. I didn't plan on sharing mimosas with a writer at a neighborhood cookie exchange, didn't plan to be teary eyed at my daughter's birthday party realizing this gathering of incredible women was NOT random at all but rather divine providence, didn't plan on the neighbor across the way having the sweetest girls for my daughter to play with, and didn't plan for her to bring a special ornament my way just minutes before we left for my hubby's third clinical trial treatment.

Nope. I did NOT plan ANY of that.

Ridiculous pain. Ridiculous joy. Ridiculous unexpected life. We don't plan any of it.

"For my thoughts are not your thoughts, neither are your ways my ways," declares the Lord. As the heavens are higher than the earth, so are my ways higher than your ways and my thoughts than your thoughts. As the rain and the snow come down from heaven, and do not return to it without watering the earth and making it bud and

flourish, so that it yields seed for the sower and bread for the eater, so is my word that goes out from my mouth: It will not return to me empty, but will accomplish what I desire and achieve the purpose for which I sent it. You will go out in joy and be led forth in peace; the mountains and hills will burst into song before you, and all the trees of the field will clap their hands. Instead of the thorn bush will grow the juniper, and instead of briers the myrtle will grow. This will be for the Lord's renown, for an everlasting sign, that will endure forever." – Isaiah 55: 8-13

35

TWO MONTHS OF MEDICAL UPDATES

February 8, 2019

Life has gotten out of hand with all the medical stuff these past two months. There is so much happening that I can't keep up my routine of writing a medical update infused with insight and inspiration every time we have news. I've been debating what to do, and although this goes against every fiber of my being, I've decided to share a series of updates that are strictly medical. Because I know people are checking in on our family. Because people who are experiencing choroidal melanoma, ocular melanoma, uveal melanoma and all the metastatic versions have found this story, and I am committed to keeping it complete so the journey is captured in its entirety. With that in mind, here are medical updates from the past two months.

Medical Update 11.27.2018

Good news and lots of updates. We just got home from two full days of screening. Seth had three rounds of blood work, an ECG, a meeting with the nurse who heads up the

IMCgp100 clinical trial, a lengthy tour of the hospital and facilities, an ultrasound-guided liver biopsy, urine analysis, and a CT scan with oral contrast. The head doctor, head nurse, and medical monitor for the research study met today to discuss Seth's case, review all the data, and make a final determination. It was an incredibly long and grueling day, but we made it through and got the good news around 4:00 p.m. that Seth has been officially accepted into the IMCgp100 clinical trial and can begin treatment on Monday, December 3rd! Seth is now off all Prednisone. The research team told us they'd need Seth off Prednisone for two full weeks before he could start treatment, but it was determined that the lead doctor had leeway within study guidelines to give the go ahead to start sooner since Seth is off Prednisone and it wasn't used to treat a brain condition. Weekly infusions of IMCgp100 will be administered indefinitely, until the treatment isn't working anymore or side effects are too severe to continue. The first three treatments will require inpatient hospitalization and the fourth treatment might require inpatient hospitalization. After that, it will be administered on an outpatient basis. We are grateful for my dad who came to stay with us early-mid November, and Seth's parents who came to stay with us mid-late November. My mom is flying out and will be here for 3 1/2 weeks to help during these first treatments. A meal train is up and running for anyone who wants to help out with meals, random household tasks, child care, transportation, and miscellaneous needs. I will be spending the next three days doing a whole host of random tasks in preparation for treatment starting, and Seth will spend the next three days getting ready for a month-long leave of absence from work. Thank you all for your concern, love, care, support, and prayers. We are blessed and surprised by your generosity and kindness.

Medical Update 12.3.2018

After four months with no treatment, the first infusion of the clinical trial drug, IMCgp100, is now complete! Seth was admitted to the hospital at 7:30 this morning in preparation for the infusion. He will be here until at least 10:00 tomorrow morning. Side effects typically set in 4-6 hours after the infusion, so now we are waiting around for side effects to set in. This morning, there has been a fair amount of discussion about the pros and cons of getting a port placed for ease of infusions and blood draws, but also in case of emergencies such as significant drops in blood pressure. No decision yet. It's up to Seth. My mom flew in yesterday and will be staying with the kids for these first four weekly infusions. Our first dinner was delivered last night before we left; it was delicious and perfectly timed. Prayers that Seth's side effects won't be too severe, that we will figure out a long-term plan for child care once my mom leaves, that Seth's body responds favorably to the IMCgp100 clinical trial drug, that he is able to stay on it as long as possible, and that the 15 tumors in his liver stabilize or shrink (40% chance of some level of shrinkage; another 10-15% of people see stabilization). Thank you for your prayers and encouragement for Seth and our family as we continue to fight metastatic uveal melanoma. God bless you all.

Medical Update 12.10.2018

Seth's port was placed this morning, and IMCgp100 infusion #2 wrapped up around 12:35 p.m. Similar to last week, Seth will be in the hospital until tomorrow mid-late morning. Typically, side effects start kicking in four to six hours after the infusion is done, but last week, Seth's side effects didn't start until 10 hours later. Severe nausea treated with IV anti-nausea meds caused severe whole-body restlessness which took a couple hours to clear before he was able to sleep. He experienced low blood pressure, fever, body aches, headache, pink sunburned-looking skin, dry and itchy skin all week, and slightly sore forearms all week. We'll see what this week's infusion brings. Hoping and praying that this treatment is effective in shrinking or stabilizing the 15 liver tumors, and that

Seth is able to stay in the trial as long as possible. Thank you for your kindness, your love, and your support.

Medical Update 12.17.2018

It was a long and difficult week between treatments, but yesterday Seth was back to his normal self. IMCgp100 clinical trial treatment #3 is DONE! We are in the hospital waiting for side effects to kick in. The first week, side effects kicked in 10 hours post-infusion. Last week after the second infusion, side effects kicked in five hours post-infusion. We are currently sitting 1 1/2 hours post infusion, and everything is still fine and dandy. This is Seth's last scheduled inpatient hospitalization for this clinical trial. If everything goes okay today and tomorrow, infusions will continue indefinitely, every week on Mondays on an outpatient basis until it stops working or side effects are too severe to continue. We appreciate all the amazing support and kindness everyone has extended during this six-month journey through metastatic uveal melanoma. Requesting prayers for a better week for Seth this week. Thanks, everyone.

Medical Update 12.24.2018

It's 11:00 a.m. on Christmas Eve and we just finished Seth's 4th IMCgp100 treatment. Metastatic uveal melanoma does not take a break for Christmas! We'll be heading home shortly and anticipate that side effects will kick in by about 3:00 p.m. We are praying for 1) Side effects to happen even though it's Christmas Eve, because side effects mean the drug is working the way it should. 2) Side effects won't be too debilitating. 3) That Seth will be able to enjoy SOME of Christmas Eve and ALL of Christmas Day with me, my mom, and our three kids. 4) That Seth will have a good week between Christmas and New Year's. 5) That he will be prepared to return to work four days a week starting January 2nd, and that transition back to work will go smoothly as we continue traveling for weekly clinical trial treatments. May the Lord bless you and keep you close this Christmas. Thank you all for your love, prayers, and kindness.

Medical Update 12.31.2018

Clinical trial treatment IMCgp100 #5 is now complete! The two big kids came with us this week since they're still on break and we wanted an opportunity to demystify the experience for them at least a little. Last night, Seth and Cooper went to a basketball game after we arrived, and Elsa and I ate at an Italian restaurant. The worst of last week's side effects set in 8 1/2 hours post infusion and lasted for 5 1/2 hours. Today, we're hoping for a lessening of side effects since it's New Year's Eve and we'd like to enjoy some time with the kids. We'd also like side effects to start lessening more quickly now because Seth returns to work this Wednesday and is hoping to pull off a four-day work week if possible. Thanks, ya'll, for your love, prayers, and support. Happy New Year!

Medical Update 1.7.2019

Seth's weekly clinical trial treatment continues. IMCgp100 #6 is now complete! Last week, side effects were minimal with the exception of nausea, headache, and terrible itching that kept him awake during the night. Seth was on full-time short-term disability all of December, returned to work on Wednesday, and will go on intermittent short-term disability starting this week with a four-day work week. His first three days back at work went surprisingly well, the best and most normal three days we've had since October. Saturday and Sunday, Seth was back to his "new normal" with more fatigue and needing to keep his activity level and rest in check. The first set of scans since starting this new treatment is scheduled for January 27th. Please pray that this treatment is effective, that scans will show stabilization or shrinkage of the 15 liver tumors. Pray for continued energy for Seth's four-day work week. Pray for endurance, health, clarity, and peace for me as caregiver. Pray for endurance for us as a couple and family as we realize the weight of indefinite weekly travel for treatment. Thanks to everyone who has helped out with meals, love and prayers from a distance, child care, and financial contributions so we can make it through this time of uncertainty. God bless you all.

Medical Update 1.14.2019

Seth just finished IMCgp100 clinical trial treatment #7. Last week's side effects were similar to the week prior and were much more manageable. Seth laid low in bed all Monday night after we got home. This was his first four-day work week on intermittent short-term disability. It was a long week, but everything went fine. Seth is due for another follow-up appointment for his primary eye tumor, so I am working on getting a referral and clinic notes sent so we can transfer care and get scheduled with a new provider in Portland. The biggest prayer request moving into the next two weeks is that scans on January 27th show stabilization or shrinkage of the 15 liver tumors. Thank you very much.

Medical Update 1.28.2019

Yesterday, Seth had the first set of scans since he started the clinical trial, IMCgp100, for metastatic uveal melanoma. GOOD NEWS! There are still 15 tumors in the liver, but no new tumors have developed since his last scans early November. They only shared details about two of the biggest lesions. The central lesion is "more necrotic," meaning it looks like some of the tissue is "dying away." The other target lesion is stable. So we will continue weekly infusions until the next set of scans in eight weeks and will go from there. We will keep on keeping on! In other news, we went out for a special fondue dinner last night after scans. We purposely stayed away from all seafood because of Seth's fish and shellfish allergies, but this morning, Seth woke up with swollen eyes, swollen lips, and must have had a swollen tongue because his speech was impacted. We reported the incident to three providers here at the cancer institute. They checked with Dr. C who gave permission for Seth to proceed with infusion #9, but did give him Benadryl and want him to take it for the next few days. Thanks, everyone, for your care, concern, love, prayers, and tangible gifts of support to keep us going during this journey. Thanks and praise God for giving us more time.

Medical Update 2.4.2019

Clinical trial IMCgp100 infusion #10 is done. We're waiting through a series of post-infusion vitals, Seth's port will be de-accessed, then we will be cleared to make the drive home. Today happens to be World Cancer Day, so let me take a moment to provide a little education on Seth's specific type of cancer. Every year, 6 in 1 million people are diagnosed with uveal melanoma. 50% of those patients experience metastasis, so the type of metastatic melanoma we are experiencing is INCREDIBLY RARE. Seth's cancer is considered an orphan cancer, meaning it is so rare that it doesn't get much attention or funding for research. But as far as we know and have been told, the trial he is on is specific to his diagnosis of metastatic uveal melanoma. We are grateful that he is able to continue on this trial for the next eight weeks, and we are hoping he will be able to continue for another eight weeks after that and beyond! In other news, Seth landed a huge deal at work this week, so it is possible to live with metastatic uveal melanoma and make major business deals at the same time. Way to go, Seth!

36

YOU DON'T HAVE TO LOVE EVERY MOMENT OF YOUR LIFE

February 20, 2019

Mama's standing behind her boss baby, steadying and straightening her on the balance beam. Another mama's wearing baby one while trying to take a photo of curly-haired baby two who's not having a second of sitting still. Girls smile in delight, jumping and falling in synchrony on the trampoline. Two push a third in a contraption that looks like a hamster wheel. Boys jump on ropes, flying to and fro. Tiny one tries a somersault, but can't seem to make it over an eight-inch triangle of foam. And then there's my baby on the bar. She hangs, then pushes herself high. Does a flip, then another before she dismounts. I know what she's trying to do. She wants to be like the big girl gymnasts she's seen on YouTube and Netflix, the girls who fly over bars without a hitch or a fall, the girls who are real, true gymnasts.

We're all trying to GET this right. We're all trying to DO this right. We all want to BE our best, SHOW our best, LIVE our very best life.

And that gets me thinking, that gets me remembering the cashier in the grocery store years ago. She talked of her kids, how she "enjoyed every moment." She gushed as she spoke of her love, her adoration for her littles through the years. And all I remember thinking in response to that gushing, loving, enjoying-every-moment mom was that I was doing my best. All I could do was do my best. I was doing my best.

And that gets me thinking, that gets me remembering all the ways I've tried to live and enjoy every moment the past eight months since Seth's diagnosis of stage IV metastatic uveal melanoma. But the truth is, I can't write a sappy letter that'll go viral and tell you all the ways you need to love and live and gush on your life every single moment of every single day. Because in the past eight months, I've learned that's not humanly possible. A lovely, lively, gushy post about living in the moment and loving every moment of your life wouldn't be authentic coming from me. Perhaps I'm overly in touch with reality, but I refuse to perpetuate the lie. Living and loving every single moment of life to the fullest is not possible, people. What is possible is to try our best, to be available, to listen, to enjoy moments and be present when we're mentally, emotionally, and spiritually able, and to do our best, but realize we're human, too.

I am doing my best. I am trying to enjoy every moment as much as humanly possible. I'm trying to look at my husband a little longer. I'm trying to listen a little harder. I am trying to hold his hand when I might not have otherwise. I am trying to stay positive, and I'm trying to be intentional about having meaningful and fun conversations on our way to and from treatment. I'm trying to make our household a place he wants to come home to, and I've done a pretty darn good job of making our bedroom a haven for when he's in bed longer than any of us would like. I've tried to savor the tiniest of moments – the sound of his voice, the way he hugs our littlest when she's loving him so hard, the way he tells our thirteen-year-old he's proud of her, how he loves the way she loves to get her nails done, the way he checks in on our son when he's playing video games and is too busy to provide a meaningful response. I take note of how it feels to be a family of five, to have this opportunity to be whole, to live as one family unit for this moment in time.

I am doing my best. I am trying my best to be the best mom I can be. I am trying to be sensitive. I am trying to give the kids space. I am trying to meet their physical needs, their emotional needs, their mental, social, and spiritual needs. I'm trying to pray before as many meals as possible, but I don't want them all to be canned prayers, so I'm trying to make sure we throw in hand and heart-spun prayers, too. I am trying to love our kids in new and fresh ways because I don't know what the future holds, and I want the very best life for each one of them. I'm encouraging daddy-daughter and father-son dates because I want our kids to have special moments with dad. But I want them to live normal lives and have normal childhood memories, too, so I'm transporting them to cheer, gymnastics, and movies with friends. I'm arranging play dates and signing up for open gymnastics. I'm allowing sleepovers with friends more than I should, and I'm letting our teenager walk or ride his bike to the grocery store to get more popcorn chicken than is necessary for any human being. I'm not enjoying every single moment, but I am trying my best. I am doing my very best. I am living life to the very best of my ability.

I don't know if I've made all the right decisions or taken all the right turns these past eight months. But I will always be able to say I did my best.

That is all ANY of us can say for certain.

I did my best.

You don't have to love every minute of your life. You don't have to savor and gush over every single moment. In fact, I promise you it's impossible. We are humans. Fallen, imperfect human beings. We cannot possibly enjoy, live, and love every single moment of every single day.

You only have to do your best, give your best, live your best, my love. You only have to sit in grace, dwell in whatever moment you're given – good or bad, good AND bad – and give thanks. God doesn't promise us a trouble-free life. He promises grace for today. That is enough, my friend. It has to be.

37

BREAKING THE
BUCKET LIST MYTH

May 6, 2019

What comes to mind when you hear the word bucket list? How about skydiving, taking a romantic trip to Paris, horseback riding at sunset, visiting the Grand Canyon, taking a hot air balloon ride, or bungee jumping? What about running a marathon, hiking to the top of Mount Everest, retiring at age 55, visiting the Great Pyramids, taking your family on an epic mission trip, or swimming with dolphins in the Caribbean? The list could go on and on, am I right?

Some people have a bucket list before they've barely left the nest. Some begin drafting a list in their 20s when life feels full of possibility. Others crack open the idea book when they're pushing retirement and they're finally free to do the things they've been waiting to do. Others never think a second about a bucket list until the reality of mortality hits home. And then there are some who never dream, never allow themselves to think beyond the here and now, never once write a single item on their so-called bucket list.

Whether you have a bucket list or not, we all know what a bucket list is. A list of activities and experiences you'd like to have before you die. Bucket list items are typically fresh, novel, exotic, unusual, unique experiences you've never had before. The assumption is that once you've completed a bucket list item, you can check it off and move on to the next one.

Today, I'm going to break the bucket list myth. Perhaps it'll inspire you to think differently about bucket lists. Perhaps it'll inspire you to actually make a bucket list if you don't already have one. Perhaps it'll free you to add something to your list you never thought of before. I don't know exactly what this post will do for you, but my ultimate aim in sharing is to help you think differently about living and dying well.

Since Seth was diagnosed with stage IV metastatic uveal melanoma 11 months ago, I've experienced the whole gamut of thoughts and feelings as his wife of nearly 21 years. Fairly early on, I felt like we should be making a special point to do special things. Maybe not bucket list items, per se, but special activities like local outings and adventures with our kids. Every time it was a weekend, I'd ask Seth if there was anything special he'd like to do. Want to go to the glass gardens? Want to go to Leavenworth, a Bavarian mountain town, for an overnight with the kids? Want to go skiing? Want to take a ferry to an island? I don't know. I was up for doing something special as a family, something to make memories. Maybe I was trying to create a bucket list for my husband? Dare I say YES?

The odd thing is that my husband would just keep responding to my random bucket list inquiries with, "No, I just want to stay home, lie low, and do the things we'd normally do as a family."

I'll be honest. This kind of bothered me at first. It still kind of bothers me. But when you're 11 months into a stage IV diagnosis, you start to understand things you never thought you'd understand. For some reason, I've begun to understand my husband's thought process. I'm not fully there, but I'm beginning to understand, I'm beginning to see the beauty in it. And that's exactly why I'm sharing today.

You see, he didn't want to check off a bunch of bucket list items in light of his diagnosis. In fact, I'm not sure if he really even had a bucket list! Several months after the diagnosis and several months of me asking him, "Do you want to....," "How about we...." "What do you think about...." and him continuing to respond with, "No, I just want to stay home, lie low, and do the things we'd normally do as a family," I finally decided to get more pointed in my questioning. After all, it seemed weird that he didn't want to do ANYTHING and I wasn't convinced he wanted to just sit at home ALL the time! So I asked again, a little differently this time, "Is there anything specific you have on your bucket list?" "Is there anything you really want to do?"

And that's when the answer came, a simple, two-point bucket list. "Well, I guess I'd like to go whale watching and take another Disney trip."

So when Seth's brother was visiting in early April, we went whale watching and completed bucket list item #1! It was fabulous and oh so good to see him smile. And I got to see the promise of a rainbow and clear skies just as we were about to board the boat, despite a forecast of nearly 100% rain.

After whale watching, all that remained on the two-point bucket list was take another Disney trip. Yay! Disney! Yahoo! The most magical place on earth. So exciting. So fun. Awesome trip for the kids. YES. All yes.

(But here's where we're breaking the bucket list myth.)

You see, we've had the blessing of going on many Disney trips. In fact, if you look back on our near 21-year marriage, the one vacation we've returned to time and time again is Disney. Our first trip to Walt Disney World was when we were on our honeymoon. Then a one-day visit to Magic Kingdom in 2002 when I was pregnant with our first child. Our first family-of-four trip was to Walt Disney World in 2010, and we loved it so much we went back and did it all over again in 2011. In 2013, we joined my husband in Los Angeles for a big work event and added a couple days at the end to take the kids to Disneyland. 2015 marked our first trip to Walt Disney World as a family of five. In 2016, right before my dad had a lung transplant, my husband and I snuck away for a short Disney cruise preceded by a single day at Magic Kingdom. And in the summer of 2017, when Seth was laid off, he won a weight loss competition and a free trip to Florida. We had one magical day at Magic Kingdom that summer before moving to Seattle.

So here we are. About to embark on yet another Disney vacation. This time, it's an official bucket-list vacation. It's not about the novelty at all. This is my husband's grandest version of "I just want to stay at home, lie low, and do something we'd normally do as a family." Okay, we're not staying home, we're not going to lay low, but we ARE very much doing the thing we've done as a family since this family was established in June of 1998.

What's the point? You might need to rethink that bucket list of yours. If you aren't inspired by the standard bucket list, if you're not the bucket list type, then maybe you've been thinking about it all wrong. What if the thing you'd want to do if you were dying is the thing you love and have been doing forever? What if the thing you'd want to do if you were dying is the most mundane thing in the world, but it means the world to you? What if that bucket list item is something you've done 25 times, but you'd really like to do it one more time because it was so incredibly good?

So what's it going to be for you? What's going to be added onto your bucket list now that we've dismembered the whole concept of bucket list? Going to visit your granddaughter one more time? Visiting that special beach one more time? Going to Mexico one more time? Reading your favorite book one more time? Running a marathon one more time? Going to lunch with that awesome friend one more time? Enjoying a chocolate bar one more time because it's so incredibly satisfying? I don't know what it is for you. But this I know for sure.

We must live well and die well. Live and die well, my friend. Every day like it's your last, or at least as much as you can muster. Whether you ride wild horses, coo with your grand-baby, or take another moment to put your feet up on the couch and count your blessings one more time, your story is going to be awesome.

38

A ONCE-IN-A-LIFETIME INVITATION

May 23, 2019

The first day of Seth's bucket list trip to Walt Disney World with stage IV metastatic uveal melanoma didn't start out quite so magical. We arrived at the gates of Magic Kingdom bright and early. I'd timed everything perfectly so we'd be there for the park's 9:00 a.m. opening. Everything was going great until we scanned our magic bands to get in and discovered that our five-day park tickets had expired, and we hadn't even been to one park yet. "This should be easy," they said. "No problem," they said. "We'll just take you over here to guest services and they'll take care of this for you." After waiting in a line and another 15 minutes at guest services with a cast member on the phone with our resort, our five-day park tickets were finally valid and ready to go.

Did I mention that I grumbled a bit while we were waiting patiently (and not-so-patiently) at the guest services desk? "All they need to do is change ONE date for FIVE people and this will be solved. Walt would find this unacceptable,"

I said. "The people in this line should be top priority of the whole park right now. These peoples' days aren't starting out magical at all. Walt would do everything he could to make this experience as quick, as easy, and as magical as possible." Breathing slowly and looking away from the cast member whose extended phone call was causing me slight first-day-of-vacation agitation, I reminded myself that we weren't entitled to magical beginnings just because my husband has stage IV cancer.

After the ticket debacle was resolved, we made our way to another guest services building where we signed up for disability access service, then continued down Main Street. Who doesn't love Main Street at Magic Kingdom? If anything will cheer you up and get you feeling good, it's Main Street and that spectacular castle. We stopped for a photo with the Disney photographer. Then one teen wanted individual pictures by the castle and they didn't quite turn out the way she wanted, so we had to take more and then a few more. Then one teen was getting grumpy from "too many pictures" and Seth said, "Yeah, maybe let's get going and not take pictures for a while." Phew. Breathe deeply. It's okay, people. Maybe the morning didn't start out perfectly magical, but it's all good. Let's regroup and make our way to Adventureland! It's time for an adventure!

We regrouped successfully. As we made our way to the entrance of Adventureland, we approached two cast members wearing Disney pin trading satchels.

(Note: Had we not made all those stops prior to this moment, we wouldn't have had such an incredibly magical day. So if things aren't going quite the way you hoped, keep moving. Life might not seem totally magical now, but it will in time. Just wait and see.)

Back to the cast members wearing Disney pin trading satchels who we approached so we could look at their pins and make our first trades of the trip. It was an ordinary interaction for a while. My husband traded a pin with one of the cast members. Then our youngest made a trade. Normally, at that point, we'd say thanks and move along with our adventure in Adventureland. But these cast members wanted to know more about us. **Where were we from?** We scored some bonus points when we said we were from Seattle because one of the cast members was from Seattle and she knew exactly where we live! **Were we planning on going to the parade this afternoon? Do we want to know some inside secrets about where the best place is to view the parade?** Brick, the other cast member, broke out a map, showed us the parade route, circled the best place for us to view and explained why.

At that point, I was moving into writer zone. Writers know what I'm talking about, that moment you realize a story is unfolding. To me, this was a story about a man named Brick who was deeply committed to his work at Magic Kingdom. This was a story about a man who loved his work, loved this place, and wanted to invest every second he could into every family who approached him to give them the most magical day they could have. I wanted to know more about this Brick and what made him so passionate about his job. I love people who love what they do.

Brick was taking a LOT of time with us, an unusual amount of time, I have to say. In nearly 21 years of going to Disney as a married couple and as a family, we hadn't had this much personal interaction with a cast member. Like I said, I thought it was a little odd, but let him keep chatting with us and engaging with us. This, after all, is the magic of Disney.

We admired Brick's favorite pins on his hat, and he told us a little about his 29-year career at Disney. But then. BUT. THEN. Brick brought conversation back to the parade, asked us to show him how we're going to wave at the parade as it comes down the street. Okay??? We all waved for him, some of us a little more excitedly than others. Again, it was a little odd, but we all complied and engaged Brick kindly and graciously as we would anyone else. I don't recall exactly how or exactly what words he used, but it was at that point that Brick asked us the question of all questions. "Do you think you could wave like that in the parade? I want to invite you to be the Grand Marshals of our parade today!"

Oh, my goodness. Tears streamed from my eyes instantly. "Oh, my goodness. You have no idea," I said to Brick as I looked at Seth and gently touched his arm. "That would be AMAZING because he has stage IV cancer." Everyone beamed with excitement as Brick proceeded to give us instructions as to where to meet, at what time, and how this Grand Marshal thing was all going to happen.

As we left Brick that morning, we wondered how in the world this incredible, amazing, magical thing had happened to us. Only God. Yes, only God could make such a thing happen. Brick had no idea about Seth's stage IV metastatic uveal melanoma diagnosis, but God did. God ordained our every step. Had our timing been different that morning, Brick and his colleague would have picked a different family as Grand Marshals. But there we were at the perfect place at the perfect time picked perfectly for this incredible, once-in-a-lifetime experience as Grand Marshals of the Festival of Fantasy Parade at Magic Kingdom. Oh. My. Goodness. This was only God.

I don't really have much else to say. I'll let the video tell the rest of the story. But here's what I want you to know. I cried half to 2/3 of the way through that parade. Why? Because the experience was completely overwhelming, "surreal" as my husband so accurately stated. As we made our way down the parade route, God revealed to me that he will provide for us, even in the midst of our darkest, deepest trials. Second, and even more important, He has a heavenly home prepared for us and it is going to be grand and wild and magical beyond our imagination. Us being Grand Marshals in a Disney parade was a once-in-a-lifetime God-ordained experience that 99.9% of people won't ever have. BUT I promise you, God has extended you an even grander invitation, an invitation to ride in His chariot, to enter His gates, to ride to the palace where streets are gold, where everything is good, and tears are no more. Accept the invitation and He will give you the ride of your life. They'll wave and He'll smile. Well done, good and faithful servant. Well done.

To view the video from our experience as Grand Marshals in Disney's Festival of Fantasy parade, visit: https://youtu.be/1SalVF8HExg.

39

THIS IS NOT NORMAL

June 13, 2019

This week marks one year since Seth's diagnosis of stage IV metastatic uveal melanoma. What started in January 2015 as one single tumor in his eye metastasized to 8-10 tumors in his liver in June 2018 and is now 16 tumors in June 2019. We started treatment at Mayo Clinic in Minnesota, moved to Seattle Cancer Care Alliance in Washington, and are currently receiving treatment at Providence in Oregon. The first-line treatment, an immunotherapy combination of Yervoy and Opdivo, was deemed to be ineffective after three infusions. After a four-month break from treatment due to a whole-body rash, a rare case of drug-induced lupus, and elevated liver enzymes that needed to be managed with steroids, we began a new treatment, this time a phase II clinical trial called IMCgp100. Infusions have been weekly for more than six months now. Most recent scans showed the presence of a new tumor in the liver, so we may be moving towards another new treatment this summer or fall.

I watch a piece of cotton drift through the air. Another piece lands on my forearm. Birds take flight overhead. The dogwood we planted in memory of Seth's grandmother is slowly losing its creamy white blooms, and the slip and slide is drip drying on a wicker chair. Tiny voices giggle and squeal on the other side of the fence. Our kids have their last full day of school today, then after a few hours tomorrow, they'll be home for summer. Life goes on. Life is normal. And not so normal at all.

And I think of that special someone, that someone who rang the doorbell of our Seattle suburb home less than a month after Seth's metastasis diagnosis last summer. She showed up with a feast of Stan's Bar-B-Q, chocolate cupcakes, and a bouquet of flowers purchased by our friends from Minnesota, hand-delivered at their request. I'll forever be in awe over that grand gesture of kindness and creativity from those Minnesota friends.

The grand gestures of kindness and creativity didn't stop there. That special someone didn't have any connection to us beyond our one mutual friend in Minnesota, yet she kept showing up, no longer at the direction of our friend back in Minnesota, but out of her own goodwill.

She delivered pizza, Jersey Mike's subs, and Thai twice. She had Mexican ready for pick up, showed up with numerous bags of groceries for a Thanksgiving feast with my in-laws, and delivered an IHOP breakfast early one Sunday before we left for scans. She stopped by with surprises for our kids – tennis shoes for our son and an outfit for each of our daughters, hand-picked and specially chosen. I found out she was the one who left me an extravagant gift at our door. And I've certainly missed something considering all her crazy acts of selfless generosity this year.

But then there was this last delivery, our first meal delivery after scans showed a new tumor, the 16th tumor. The doorbell rang and there she was with a big bag of Chick-Fil-A.

"Oh, my goodness. Thank you. This is going to be AMAZING," I said. "How are you doing?" she asked. I went on to explain that scans showed a new tumor. She already knew from the post I'd shared on Facebook that morning. "Do you need to talk?" she inquired. "Yeah, actually."

In she came with her big white bag full of chicken sandwiches, fruit, salad, and waffle fries. She sat on the loveseat. I sat on the long couch on the opposite side of the room.

There we sat.

Facing each other.

We'd just arrived home from treatment and a three-hour drive, my husband was still out in the car on a conference call for work, and our kids were all gone, so I had a little time.

Time. That's all any of us need...just a little time.

Conversation began. I went straight at it. She'd asked me directly if I needed to talk and I said yes. So in I went, right in once we sat down. No use beating around the bush. I told her where things stood. I looked straight at her and expressed my concerns. I told her what I was needing right now.

After I expressed what I needed to express, she responded in an ever-so loving and understanding way, saying the thing I needed to hear for one whole year.

"This is not normal. This is not normal at all."

"No, it's not," I replied. Silence fell a bit before conversation moved on.

Can anybody give me an amen? This is NOT normal. This life we've led for the past year is NOT normal. If you'd like to debate the definition of "normal" for me, go for it. If you'd like to argue that "normal" is relative and nobody is normal, that's fine. Go at it. But there IS some semblance of normal, some top-of-the-bell-curve range of normal life and we have NOT been living that life this past year.

A 6 in 1 million diagnosis is NOT normal. Moving into a new home on June 11th, driving away from that new home and flying 1,700 miles away on June 13th, and leaving your kids with your in-laws for 11 days while you go get a serious diagnosis is NOT normal. Having to sit on the phone for hours and fight with insurance companies over coverage (or lack of coverage) of MRIs and PET scans when you are dealing with your husband's pending diagnosis is NOT normal. Having to stay in hotels, guest houses, and other peoples' houses while you're getting scans and treatments is NOT normal. Calling your braless friend to come over when it's still dark and drive your kid to the bus stop in her pajamas because you have to get your spouse to the ER as soon as possible and he shouldn't be left alone for even a few minutes is NOT normal. Having a rash show up ALL over your entire body is NOT normal. Having your skin turn from normal to vitiligo is NOT normal. Having your beard turn 100% gray when you're 45 years old is NOT normal. Having to travel three hours one way every Sunday night to get to a clinical trial, get an infusion, and drive back three hours every Monday for months upon months is NOT normal. Having people watch your seven-year-old and fourteen-year-old every single Sunday and Monday is NOT normal. Having to leave your sixteen-year-old to fend for himself every Sunday and Monday is NOT normal. Having your seven-year-old cry for two months on Sundays because having her mom and dad leave every Sunday is getting really old and she's had enough of it is NOT normal. Having scans every eight weeks is NOT normal. Going to get your blood tested every week is NOT normal. Worrying whether a teeny tiny box titled "joint ownership with survivorship" is checked on the title on all of your vehicles is NOT normal. Being told your spouse has another tumor, waiting too long for a response from the doctor, and being told it is highly advised to wait another five weeks until the next set of scans to see how the melanoma is growing, and that he might need another biopsy or he might need a PET scan and that there might be six or more next treatment options is NOT normal. Finishing a workout and having to lean over a garbage can as you walk into the locker room because a wave of grief washed over you as you took a sip of water and you know that if you can't keep that grief contained you just might spit it all out into that garbage can. Yeah. Not normal.

This is NOT normal.

Thank you, special someone who has diligently served us with meals and unexpected gifts this year, for straight up acknowledging the ONE simple thing I needed to hear.

This is NOT normal.

This is not normal at all.

I've tried. I've REALLY tried to live a normal life. Although metastatic uveal melanoma rarely strays from my mind, I've worked hard for 12 long months to keep my thought life tamed and at bay. I have worked hard to live a normal life for myself, my husband, and our three children. I have worked hard to be as positive as I can, to enjoy every moment and not worry about this, that and everything under the sun.

I've seen Seth looking normal, acting normal, and working hard just like everything is normal. I've watched him put in long hours at work and go on business trips. During this past year, he made an appearance on the red carpet of the Billboard Music Awards and someone commented so poignantly, "This is your best work life ever." Yes. True. These past several months HAVE been his best work life ever. I want a good work life for my husband. I want an awesome work life for him. I honor and respect the supernatural power of positivity he has had in response to his diagnosis. I want a joyful and normal life for our entire family. But I also need to acknowledge that this is NOT normal.

So thank you, special someone. Thank you for saying it straight up.

This is NOT normal.

I just needed someone to say that.

I just needed someone to see that.

I just needed to know I wasn't alone in thinking this is NOT normal.

When you sit with someone's story and acknowledge that this is NOT normal, you validate their pain, you validate their life.

And here's what you really need to know. Yes, this is a

secret I believe everyone does NOT understand intuitively. When you listen to someone, when you really sit and listen to their story and acknowledge that this is NOT normal, you free them to truly live.

So yes. Thank you, special someone. Thank you for listening and acknowledging. Thank you for saying, "This is not normal. This is not normal at all." Thank you for sitting in that loveseat, looking at me, and saying it like you meant it.

Your words validated me. Your words reminded me that I'm not alone, that I'm not going mad. Your words reminded me that there are people who understand and are willing to sit with me and the questions. Best yet, your words were empowering. Your words allowed me to embrace my gut feeling that this is indeed NOT normal. Your words empowered me to move on, to soak in the sun, the clouds, the rain, and the gentle breeze. Your words freed me to live, knowing it's okay to fully acknowledge pain and fully acknowledge life in its bountiful abundance. Your words freed me to leave my seven-year-old with my fourteen and sixteen-year-old last night so I could go to Bible Study and discuss how we can best be light in the darkness. Your words freed me to be vulnerable with the group, to share prayer requests for myself and for our family. Your words freed me to make a quick stop at home and grab the car keys, trusting that these kids are going to be okay, because light will always overcome darkness. Your words – THIS IS NOT NORMAL – freed me to put those keys in the ignition and drive to my monthly girls' night where I was greeted with a hug, six welcoming smiles, and genuine conversation with the most amazing ladies yet. Your words – THIS IS NOT NORMAL – freed me to breathe easy while I sipped a glass of wine, ate Ghirardelli chocolates, talked about motherhood, work life, and lots of 40-something normal things for two hours. Your words – THIS IS NOT NORMAL – allowed me to see, once again, that life is full of incredible pain and incredible beauty. And as daylight turned to darkness, she turned on the lights and our normal, ordinary, everyday conversation lit up the darkness.

40

LIVING EIGHT
WEEKS AT A TIME

August 22, 2019

A new tumor showed up in Seth's liver at his eight-week scans in May. But the rest of the tumors showed a mix of shrinkage, growth, and stabilization, so we signed a form stating we were choosing to continue the clinical trial despite disease progression and proceeded to receive eight more infusions.

At his eight-week scans in July, the new tumor grew, and a couple other concerning ones grew a tad, too. But just like last time, the rest of the tumors showed a mix of shrinkage, growth, and stabilization, so we did a risk analysis with the doctor and decided it made most sense to stay on study for another eight weeks.

After those scans, I shared a medical update with friends and family. One response caught my attention more than any other and has stuck with me since.

"I can't imagine living eight weeks at a time."

Reality is, we started living scan to scan 4 ½ years ago when Seth was first diagnosed with choroidal melanoma, but living scan to scan took on a whole new meaning eight months ago when we started a trial to treat the metastatic tumors. Instead of scans every nine months, six months, four months, or three months as we'd done in the past, this trial required scans every eight weeks. So when I saw that "I can't imagine living eight weeks at a time" comment pop up, it resonated deep within. Living in eight-week intervals is a challenge. It changes the way you live.

We've been living eight weeks at a time for more than eight months now. But this current eight-week period felt different. Both Seth and I had prepared ourselves that there might have been enough tumor growth for us to be kicked out of the trial back in July. So when they told us we could stay on for another eight weeks, it felt like a GIFT, a gift of more time.

Seth was glad he had another eight weeks to stay on a treatment that's become predictable as far as regimen and side effects. This is a crazy busy time for him at work. He had three big business trips over the course of this eight-week period, for a total of 11 full days of out-of-state travel. During these eight weeks, he also took on more responsibility at work. And then there's the four-day Boundary Waters trip he's had planned with buddies, also during this eight-week period. He decided he wanted to put more priority on friendship, so he shared his intentions of getting a guys' night out scheduled sooner rather than later. And he thinks we should be doing a better job of inviting more people over for dinner, so we agreed on a family we wanted to invite over for dinner. The only problem is we haven't gotten around to inviting them yet. They're the ones texting us, asking if we have room for freezer meals.

Living life eight weeks at a time has taught us that despite our challenges, despite our most difficult hardships, life goes on. There's work to be done, schedules to keep, priorities to consider, and plans to be made. So we flow, we live, and we move through life. We keep things as normal as possible for normal is predictable, normal is comforting, normal is known.

The day we received scan results in July, I knew this eight-week period was a gift and I have treated it as such. Some might say I've gone overboard. Maybe so. But right now, I care little for what people think unless they've walked in my shoes. I've done what I needed to do. In July, I decided that from here on out, I will do everything I can to keep myself healthy. I committed to working out three times a week, went to the dentist, to the OBGYN for a pap smear, had my annual mammogram, an intake appointment with a grief counselor, an intake appointment with a nutritionist, and met with a primary care physician. Have we covered all the bases? In this eight-week period, I created an aggressive agenda and took a whole five-day work week, 9 a.m. to 4 p.m., while my girls were at cancer camp to analyze my work life and seriously consider my call to pursue writing and photography in light of current circumstances. I pressed hard on household tasks, ensuring two furnace parts were replaced under warranty, ensuring a claim is still in process for replacing our washing machine also under warranty, beginning a discussion about cutting the cable cord, and keeping up on laundry, cleaning, and finances so things were ready in the event of sudden change. And yes, I did all of that with the overarching goal of being a good wife to a husband balancing work and stage IV cancer, a good mom to three kids home for summer, and the best friend possible to local women who have been absolutely fabulous in every way possible. My anxiety has increased, and I've hit a few walls of fatigue and stress. But I've also felt strong and empowered and I will somehow make it through this.

Living life eight weeks at a time has taught us that keeping ourselves healthy isn't optional, it's necessary. Taking responsibility for stuff that needs to get done isn't optional, it's necessary. Sometimes it takes hardships to push us to do the things we've been debating, doubting, and putting off for far too long. Yes, there's no better time than NOW to do pretty much everything.

And then there are the kids. I brought the girls back-to-school shopping and our son by himself. Managed to get all three out for school supply shopping, our annual pizza at the park outing, and an afternoon at a trampoline park. During this eight-week period, one of our son's best friends moved to California. I prayed that God would surround our son with new friends and that existing friendships would be strengthened, and that prayer has definitely been answered. As evidenced by empty energy drink cans, McDonald's bags on the kitchen island, and lots of voices coming from the game room, this has been an incredibly busy social summer for our son. Our oldest daughter has also been socializing like a mad woman. And then there's cheer. She had to raise $650 through fundraising in addition to the $550 we already paid for basic fees and $675 for the uniform package. In this eight-week period, she learned what it's like to go door-to-door trying to raise $650 by selling $9 car wash tickets. Real life at its finest. The youngest has been obsessed with playing. Any kind of playing. Indoor. Outdoor. Slip and slide. Playground. Movies. Playdates. Lemonade Stands. Tractor rides through elk fields. Whatever. It's all fair game. I can still carry her if she jumps into my arms, which reminds me she's still so little. And I see my big kids ready to head off to a beautiful new high school in a couple weeks, and time is literally slipping away before my eyes. I want to stop time for them. Stop time for me. Stop time for all of us as a family because this couldn't be going any faster, and I don't want to get through this medical crisis and realize they're grown, they're gone. What happened? Oh my.

Living life eight weeks at a time has taught us that there is a season for everything. Seasons come and seasons go. Seasons don't stop when you're stressed or distressed. Seasons won't stop so you can enjoy them a little longer. Savor those seasons while you can. Because once they're gone, they're gone. Love whatever season you find yourself in. Because before you know it, it'll have turned.

And I was holding up oh so (sort of) well for four weeks

and six days of this eight-week period until our fourteen-year-old daughter jumped out of the car and sprinted into the house to change out of her cheer uniform before I could process what was going on. She was leaving with her friend and needed to pack quickly. I didn't even get to say goodbye. Realizing what was happening, I looked out the side window of our car and started to cry. "Why are you crying?" Seth asked. "You should have told us your plans."

"I didn't plan this," I responded. "I didn't plan any of this." All I'd planned, all I'd hoped for was ONE meal out as a family that weekend. One meal. But five became four when our 16-year old said he had to work all day. And four became three when our daughter rushed off to a last-minute outing with a friend. And suddenly, our family time was gone and it was just the three of us with 45 minutes until I needed to leave for a photo shoot. Not enough time for a nice meal out. Arby's was where it was. I felt like Steve Martin in *Father of the Bride*[1] when the whirlwind wedding left him trapped in a crowd, unable to see his daughter for even a passing moment before she whisked away with her new husband. What happened to my daughter? What happened to my family time? What happened to my life?

Yes, that's what finally broke me. That's what made me cry. That's what living eight weeks at a time has taught me. Live diligently. Live awake. Life is a fleeting mist and we'd better get at it NOW.

I gathered myself. I ate my turkey club at Arby's. I was back in time for the photo shoot and it was awesome.

But the truth is, it had been a difficult week. My husband woke with pain on Tuesday that distressed him, and he's not a distressed kind of guy. The pain lasted all day, made him uncomfortable, worried and more fatigued than normal. The pain got better by day two, three, four, and five, but he could still feel something different in there, and there was still an area that was sensitive to touch. I sent an email to the head nurse and they told us they wanted us to come early for scans.

We didn't even get eight weeks this time. We got five instead. Just as I'd thought. This eight-week period was a gift. Every week. Every day. Every minute and second. A gift.

While this week's scans didn't show any new tumors and technically, he's stable according to study parameters (less than 20% growth since the last scans five weeks ago), the doctor said he's "on the plus side of stable." There's also a key lab that's been on the rise for seven weeks, which more often than not indicates that the melanoma is getting ready to grow. The doctor recommended we begin taking a serious look at what our next treatment options will be. Sometime in the next two to three weeks, we'll be meeting with an interventional radiologist to determine what type of liver-directed treatment will be best, and after that treatment is done, we'll need a new systemic treatment, which will likely be another clinical trial.

So for now, we will live NOT EIGHT WEEKS at a time, but ONE DAY at a time. That's the best choice any of us can make anyway.

"Therefore do not worry about tomorrow, for tomorrow will worry about itself." - Matthew 6:34

41

THERE AREN'T
ENOUGH WORDS TO
DESCRIBE CANCER

November 12, 2019

I started writing *The Apple of My Eye* back in January 2015 when Seth was diagnosed with eye cancer, back when blogging was popular and it was trendy to let your story inspire and speak for itself. But it's not 2015 anymore. Barely anyone blogs the way they used to. We're now told that if you want to serve an audience with your writing, you have to have a niche, you can't just write willy-nilly about this and that. You can't just tell your story and let others take from it what they wish. You must have a dedicated focus, a specific thing you write about, an intentional, measurable way of meeting others' most pressing need. Yes, times have changed. I don't write nearly as much for public consumption these days, and I've neglected the writing part of my website for nearly three months. I've spent lots of time getting to know my reader, but reality has restricted me from serving her as well as I know I could. The truth is, I don't have the luxury of worrying about writing and publishing trends right now. I started telling this story in January 2015; even if there are gaps bigger than I'd like, even if it's no longer trendy to tell your story and let others see its significance, I'm going to tell it anyway. I'm going to tell and keep telling this story, and I will finish what I started. This story is for me AND for you. Yes, against current prevailing beliefs, I believe that story has power, in and of itself.

Some would tell you there aren't ANY words to describe cancer. I'm here to tell you there aren't ENOUGH words to describe the cancer experience.

It's been 17 months since we found out that Seth's cancer metastasized from his eye to his liver. Three months ago, his scans were stable according to clinical trial protocol (less than 20% growth since previous scans), but they were "on the plus side of stable." A key lab that typically indicates melanoma growth had been on the rise for several weeks, and the doctor admitted we'd given this drug a "good college try." A new tumor presented itself back in May and had grown by July's scans, so we had to sign paperwork indicating we were choosing to continue treatment despite disease progression. During those months, tumor response to the study drug was more mixed than it had been, so the decision to stay on study hadn't been as clear as it once was. All of this together, it was time to consider our next-best treatment option. Since there was less than 20% growth, they allowed us to stay on study for another six weeks as we transitioned to a new treatment. There were scheduling nightmares. We met with an interventional radiologist to discuss a liver-directed procedure called Y90, had a mapping procedure, and had the actual Y90 procedure where they delivered tiny radioactive glass beads to an artery in the left lobe of his liver in an attempt to kill as many tumors along that artery as possible. We went through a full week of Seth being down and out from the procedure. Two weeks later, we were back for a CT scan. The contrast caused a severe allergic reaction and we ended up in a random ER on our way home; he was drugged up with five meds and hooked to bags of fluids in an attempt to get the contrast flushed out of his system as quickly as possible. We've waited for phone calls, waited for answers, waited for what's next, and waited to see who will help us coordinate all of this. Another Y90 is scheduled for the right lobe the day before Thanksgiving, and five days from now, we're flying to Nashville for a consultation with the clinical trial we're hoping to start AFTER the Y90 procedure. It's a never-ending story, a story that has a million words, a million turns and not nearly enough time to explain the experience it truly is.

Cancer patients and caregivers will understand. Maybe they're right? There are no words to describe cancer. On the other hand, there aren't enough words to describe cancer. I could go on and on. Oh, I have plenty of words. Just give me enough time, enough space, and I will WOW you with how complicated this journey is.

In an effort to travel this path in a way that feels lighter and easier, I'm doing it my way, documenting it my way these past 17 months. When it comes to publishing for public consumption, I'm writing significantly less than I used to. But I am committed to documenting this story to the end. I'm sharing updates and significant insights as I feel led to do so publicly, but equally important, I'm documenting this story in journals. To give you an idea of how much I've written, how much there is to say about cancer, I've filled half of a journal in less than three months. I'm sharing the condensed version, the big-picture story in *The Apple of My Eye*. The truest story is tucked away, hand-written, unedited and unfiltered in real-time ink.

I never quite understood why so many people who experienced cancer got book contracts. I mean, what's so special about cancer that it automatically necessitates a book being published? Well, let me tell you. I have conceived several books, but this journey is most definitely a book. Anyone who has gone through cancer, particularly rare and metastatic cancers like my husband's, will tell you that there is absolutely

NO way to adequately describe the true cancer experience unless you write a full-on book. So I am writing. For a while now – in fact, this whole metastatic experience – I have been writing in journals. Nobody knows the real story from my spouse and caregiver perspective except me and God. There are simply too many words to describe cancer. It's not possible without a book. So today, I declare that I am writing this real and very true story. Not for public consumption, but for my own health and well-being now, and for some unknown somebodies in the future. Whether it be our children and grandchildren, or organized later into a book that's released into the universe, I do not know. But I AM writing it.

Between now and then, you need to know that cancer not only affects you medically, but affects you physically, mentally, emotionally, spiritually, professionally, financially, relationally, socially, personally, and any other "ally" you can think of. If you've gone through cancer and disagree, then jump for joy; you've come through it a lot less war-torn than me. If you are hippy skippy everything is okay because we're going to heaven anyway, then praise the Lord; your faith is steadier than mine. Even Jesus cried out, "My God, why have you forsaken me?"[1] before his crucifixion. As for me, I will not tell you this is easy. I will not tell you this is just beautiful or just terrible. I will tell you it is ALL of these things rolled into one, all-consuming beautiful AND all-consuming terrible.

Seth is chronically tired, doesn't sleep well, is nauseous even with anti-nausea meds, sweats easily, gets full easily, and doesn't have nearly the appetite he did three months ago. But then there are days like yesterday, where we are out and about doing life as normal, and he makes it through with little complaint and little impact, and we are grateful for normal. I wax and wane with my energy levels, sleep is unpredictable, and I've gained weight I've had a tough time losing. But we work with our bodies and are beginning to understand our limits. He sleeps more, takes the maximum dosage of anti-nausea meds, and has tried alternative treatments. He eats what he can and stops when he's full. It's okay. He wanted to lose weight anyway! I let myself fall asleep on the couch while watching the Food Network Thanksgiving Cookoff if I need to, and I'm working out when I can, not beating myself up when I can't.

Seth is still sharp as a tack mentally. Cancer's not taking this man down! But I've had a bear of a time keeping thoughts of cancer blocked out for any significant amount of time. It's nearly impossible to stop thinking about cancer, and family support group has taught me I'm not alone in that. I put so much mental effort towards doing everything I can to help Seth achieve as positive outcomes as possible that I start questioning my capacity to contribute anything else good to society. But then someone applauds me for doing what I'm doing and reminds me that not everyone could research and advocate for their loved one the way I've researched and advocated for mine. And it reminds me that my mind is sound. Yes, indeed, sound.

I've said it before, and I'll say it again. Seth has a supernatural power of positivity. Emotionally, he's been a solid rock through this whole thing. I've literally only seen him break down four times this whole 17-month journey through metastatic uveal melanoma. That, in case you were wondering, is MIRACULOUS considering everything we've been through. But he has been wearing down a bit in recent months. It's the physical stuff that's taken a very slow wear on his emotions. His zip isn't quite like it used to be. He's not nearly as excited and energetic when he comes home from work at night. The signs are there. It's taking a toll, but he is STILL Superman. As for me, the emotion comes in waves. Typically, I'm much stronger, much more resilient than I expect myself to be. I think I should cry more than I do. But the emotion comes in waves. It comes, washes over me without warning. There it is. Yes, we must address these emotions emerging from such trauma. Yes, this is trauma. It's okay to cry. It's okay to feel numb. It's okay to feel all of it.

Spiritually? Well, WOW. Surprisingly, this isn't a conversation Seth and I have had a lot since his diagnosis 17 months ago. He is secure in his faith, secure he will enter heaven's gates when God calls him home. His faith doesn't waiver, at least it seems on the surface. I, on the other hand, don't even know where to start. I thought my faith was oh so secure, oh so rich, oh so full. Now, I am seeing God, Jesus, the Holy Spirit in completely new ways, and I am thinking I knew nothing before this, and am only beginning to see the real trinity. I have lots of questions, questions that won't be answered in a single post, better left between me and God, better kept for another book because these aren't easy questions, I tell you. I surrender to God's sovereignty. I read scripture regularly, but don't pray enough because my prevailing belief is that he's in control of all the final outcomes anyway. I know I should pray more. I pray short prayers, brutally honest prayers. He speaks to me in dreams, in nature, through music and people. He brings to mind bits and pieces of key scripture, revealing His intimate nature and wishes for me to press on in faith, even when it's difficult.

Seth keeps working, maintaining a 40+ hour work week and business travel while undergoing cancer treatments, breaking only when he has to. Work and cancer consume most of his energy. I press on with photography, the most promising, immediate money-making element of this creative endeavor I've undertaken the past five years. Photography sends me into a state of flow, energizes me, and allows me to be creative while helping me forget about everything else. Writing and editing for public consumption is an unpaid luxury I rarely have time for right now. And I pick up ALL the other pieces that keep a family moving – household, finances, errands, three kid stuff, the list goes on and on. I have lots of questions about work, for both me and my husband, but I am trusting we are going to make the best God-led decisions for our family each step of the way.

Work is, of course, related to finances. And cancer is, of

course, related to finances. We worry about finances, as does every family, and I watch as the medical account goes down, little by little, knowing we don't have an end in sight. But thanks to the generosity and kindness of others, we have been blessed with everything we need so far. We can tap into stocks and even retirement savings if necessary, and I'm not afraid to ask for more help when I need it. We do our best to minimize unnecessary spending, but we're not going to stop living life because of cancer.

Relationally, we're a mixed bag, only this bag seems a little more mixed than the rest. As a couple, it would be ideal if we could spend more time together, just the two of us. But the reality is, all of our time together is spent 1) doing cancer stuff, 2) sleeping or 3) having family time together which is difficult with two out of three children being teenagers. Our last non-cancer date was five months ago for our anniversary. Honestly, it's okay. We've been together 24 years, married for 21. The foundation of our marriage was built long ago.

After cancer management, the most important thing is our family. I don't know if we're doing this right, but once again, family support group has shown me that nobody who's experiencing cancer with a young family knows if they're doing it right. We try our best. We work hard, I'm telling you HARD, to find family time for normal things like meals around our table, a meal out on the weekends, one-on-one outings with kid + dad as he feels up to it, and a special family activity here and there as my husband feels well enough AND we're able to pull everyone together for any significant amount of time. It is not nearly as easy as it should be. That bothers me.

I am continually working on family time these days, yet I am beyond grateful for our support system of family and friends near and far. Circumstances have been less than ideal, but the fact that we've made such an intricate and beautiful community in a state we've only lived in for two years has been nothing short of a miracle. The meals, child care, and love we've been given have been absolutely astounding. The way we've been cared for and looked after has been noteworthy beyond belief. The daily and special events we've been invited to and participated in have been life giving, keeping our minds off hard, uncertain things.

I won't speak for Seth as to how he'd sum up this cancer experience. That's his business. As for me as wife, caregiver and mother of our three children, I feel like I'm flailing to keep life feeling as normal as possible. Sometimes life feels normal, but more often than not, it doesn't feel normal at all. I love normal moments when I forget about cancer and do whatever brings peace and joy – moments when I have fun, moments when I experience awesome conversation and perfect community, moments when everything flows in the garden, when I'm behind the camera, when I'm running to rap music, when I'm hanging with a stellar group of moms and kids on the playground after school. But cancer is waiting in the background, consuming our life, demanding my attention once again. There aren't enough words to describe cancer. But I'll try.

Thanks for listening. Thanks for loving us. Thanks for understanding.

42

SEEING ISN'T BELIEVING

January 10, 2020

Seth bumped into Maurice at LAX when he was on his way home from the American Music Awards for a business trip. Maurice, our former neighbor and father of nine. Maurice, who we ran into at parades, BBQs, church services, nights around the campfire with community, prepping for fundraisers, and random places like Walmart's baking goods aisle right before we moved from Minneapolis to Seattle. Of all the people Seth could bump into at LAX, of course it was Maurice.

"It was good to see Maurice. But you could tell there was a bit of a disconnect when he saw me," Seth admitted. Maurice and his wife had been following our story on Facebook and my website. Wherever. However. It's what we intend. To share our story. To be connected to family, friends, colleagues, and neighbors active and not-so-active in our lives anymore. To give them glimpses into this leg of our journey.

"But you could tell there was a bit of a disconnect when he saw me." I thought about that a bit. It struck me as surprising.

Disconnect.

Hmmm…

"What do you mean by disconnect?" I asked Seth.

"Well, maybe when he read your posts, he thought I was going to be a lot worse than when he saw me in real life?" responded Seth, perhaps a bit reluctant to interpret the disconnect he sensed without having asked Maurice himself.

"He and his son laid hands on me and prayed for me right there in the airport," said Seth. "We chatted for a while, caught up a bit before we parted ways. It was good."

Disconnect.

It bothered me.

I sat still in the dark of the passenger side as our car continued down the interstate to Portland for yet another clinical trial treatment, just one day after Seth had returned from his five-day business trip to the American Music Awards in Los Angeles.

Disconnect.

Ugh.

I hated it.

Disconnect.

I pondered. Overthought. Broke out my phone and began typing whatever came out of my fingers in a note to myself. Words. More words. Word after word. I don't care if this sounds good. I don't care if this is right, sounds terrible, or whatever. Just let me write it out. There is something to this disconnect that bothers me to my bones. I don't like disconnect. It's not me. It's wholly NOT me. If there's one thing, ANY thing I want to be known for, it's connection, not disconnection. Authenticity, not deceit. No beating around the bush for this gal. Disconnect? It's nothing I want to be a part of. Real. True. Authentic. Being. That's all I want to be. Forget anything that connects me to disconnection.

If anything. Any ONE thing I've tried to do is portray this cancer journey, this stage IV metastatic uveal melanoma journey as real, authentic, and true. My truest, most authentic words. My truest, most honest retelling of my side of the story, my side of this journey.

So yeah.

Disconnect.

The disconnect my husband perceived in Maurice bothered me. I didn't want Maurice to sense a disconnect between what he was seeing in Seth in real life and what I had portrayed about him in written word. If there was a disconnect, I guess it was my fault? I'm sorry. I've done my best to portray truth. But cancer is deceiving. Cancer is a deceitful beast. If anything will make you feel disconnected, if anything will make you second guess what you're seeing and hearing and experiencing, it might just be cancer. So maybe it wasn't my fault after all. My telling of the story was my telling of the story. Maurice's disconnect was just the reality of cancer coming true. Cancer looks totally normal one day and totally NOT normal the next. This is the reality of cancer. It's a walking, breathing, living beast of disconnection.

I beat my fingers on my iPhone. Yeah, I beat it out. I wrote whatever I damn well pleased. Something needed to get out. I hated the disconnect Mr. Maurice and my Seth had experienced that day at LAX.

My hubby on his way home from a five-day business trip to the AMERICAN MUSIC AWARDS, for goodness sakes, with STAGE IV CANCER. How can it get any more disconnected than that? Forgive yourself, Amy. Give yourself grace. This is a real-life disconnect. The American Music Awards don't connect with cancer. It's not your fault. These are walking disconnects. You've told the truth. Be still and know you have told your truth. You haven't gotten it wrong. Seeing isn't believing.

Fast forward to the days and weeks ahead.

Sick. Then not sick. Then sick again. Then not sick. Then really sick too far out from the procedure to possibly be tied to the procedure. What is this? Should we call? Should we not call? Should we be worried? Is this still a side effect from treatment? Something else? Who is managing this? Who's in charge? Who knows what's really going on? When should we worry? What numbers matter most? At what point do we worry about LDH, ALT, AST, Alkaline Phosphatase, Bilirubin, this and that? What do all these numbers and letters mean anyway? Doesn't it matter that this number is high? Doesn't it matter that this number had been lower and is now higher, and it's supposed to be getting lower every week? Is seeing believing? Do I believe your words when you tell me it's a treatment side effect, or do I believe my gut that tells me this is something else?

On December 17, 2019, Seth flew to Nashville for three days of screening appointments for the IDE196 clinical trial at Sarah Cannon Cancer Center we're supposed to be starting on January 2, 2020. I stayed behind this time. We decided we could spend my $820 airfare on something else. I'd join him next time. Now we only hope there is a next time.

Seth verified we'd be receiving scan results that Friday, December 20, 2019, of his Nashville trip. Fresh scans. Oh, happy day. Or not. We don't always know. Seth Face Timed me in to the call with Dr. M. Another doctor. Another day. Only this doctor was good. Very good, I tell you. The tumors on the left side of Seth's liver have mostly stayed stable with maybe a little shrinkage. One tumor on the right side grew by 1 cm, but "we don't know if it's real growth or inflammation." I've learned they like to say that. What's a person to know? If a radiologist and oncologist don't know what they're seeing, how are we supposed to know what we're dealing with as the patient and caregiver? Just asking. Who knows? Nobody really. They do their best. They're only human after all. This I know for sure. And there's a tumor in the abdominal lining. And on your rib bone. "This is the first time we've heard of the cancer spreading outside of the liver, so this is kind of big, bad news for us," Seth admitted. "Yeah," replied Dr. M. As if she was supposed to say anything else. I'm sure she said something else, but I don't recall now. Seeing and hearing aren't believing. I watched the raindrops hit my office window and drip down slowly, creating an art piece as I listened to the news from Nashville. The cancer has spread.

And yeah. His bilirubin is up. So "we'll need you to go in and get labs when you're in Minnesota for Christmas. Maybe the 30th would be good? That'll be close enough to the projected start date for the trial that we'll know if you're able to start." In just a matter of days since it had last been tested, Seth's bilirubin had crossed over 1.2 (the upper limit of normal) to 1.4. Ten days later on December 30, 2019, it was 2.4. Bilirubin jumped further to 5.3, and today on January 10, 2020, it's 5.8.

Seeing isn't believing.

Hearing isn't believing either.

Hurry. Rush. Get in for an ultrasound within 48 hours. If a bile duct is blocked, then we can put a stent in, get the bile flowing again and get these numbers down to 1.5 or lower so you can start the clinical trial in Nashville. Hurry. Rush. ASAP! This is important, big, urgent. High bili is not good. High bili isn't healthy. Bili I see. High bili.

He can't see. The ultrasound tech can't see. There are too many tumors to see a blocked duct. He literally can't see anything he needs to see.

"The ultrasound was inconclusive. You're going to need a scan," said the local doctor.

Can't have a CT scan because of increasingly severe allergic reactions to the contrast dye? Then you'll need to have a MRI.

"We just had one," we said.

"Have another," said the local doctor.

"We need to know what's going on within 48 hours," said the clinical trial doctor from a distance.

"No. Another .5 increase in bilirubin doesn't necessitate you being admitted or going into the ER for a scan over the weekend. I'll order a scan for next week. You'll hear from scheduling," said the local doctor.

Wait. Wait some more. Then wait some more while Seth's bilirubin is soaring and staying high.

Disconnect.

Hearing isn't believing.

Seeing isn't believing.

I'm not crazy. Cancer is crazy. Whatever cancer.

43

A CHANCE TO LIVE

January 31, 2020

Seth's mid-month MRI didn't bring good news. As if the December 20th bad news that the cancer had spread from his liver to the abdominal lining and rib bone wasn't bad enough, we found out on January 22nd that the cancer had become even more aggressive. There are now more tumors in the liver, the large conglomerate mass in his abdomen has become even larger, there is a new large mass in the abdomen, several lymph nodes are involved, there's the tumor on the rib bone, and now there are also several small tumors on Seth's spine. This wasn't the news we wanted. This wasn't the news we expected. This isn't the news anyone wants to hear ever.

And then there was the bilirubin issue. It had risen to an all-time high of 6.4 right around the time of that mid-month MRI; 1.2 or lower is normal. The oncologist told us blocked bile ducts might be causing Seth's bilirubin to soar, but when we went in for an ultrasound to check, it was considered inconclusive because there were too many tumors to visualize the ducts. Upon further examination of the ultrasound, the radiologist said there weren't any blocked bile ducts, but second and third opinions from surgeons suggested there were constrictions in the bile ducts and surgery should be scheduled ASAP so we have one last CHANCE at getting Seth's bilirubin down to 1.5 or lower so we can have one last CHANCE at going on the clinical trial in Nashville.

The morning of December 20, 2019, we both woke up thinking the cancer was still confined to the liver and all the labs were acceptable for a new clinical trial starting January 2, 2020. We woke this morning, the morning of January 31, 2020, and my husband is now on full-time short-term disability, the cancer has spread all over his body, and we can't start any trial or treatment unless his bilirubin can get from a current 4.7 to 1.5 or lower.

"There's a CHANCE we could get on a trial."

"There's also a CHANCE this could go downhill fast."

We chose to take a CHANCE. We chose to have surgery to place stents in Seth's bile ducts. We chose to do it on Friday instead of waiting until Wednesday so we'd have a CHANCE at getting the bilirubin down sooner rather than later, a CHANCE to get on the trial sooner rather than later, a CHANCE to get treatment for the tumors sooner rather than letting them grow more.

"Do you think we should meet with palliative care?"

I chose to take a CHANCE, to ask the question that no doctor, no nurse practitioner, no nurse, no medical assistant, no social worker, no NOBODY had EVER asked us in 19 plus months of dealing with this incredibly rare cancer called metastatic uveal melanoma. I chose to take a CHANCE on behalf of my husband, on behalf of myself, on behalf of our children and our families. I chose to take a CHANCE when I asked this question because for four months, I KNEW in the depths of my gut that nobody was properly managing the symptoms and side effects Seth was experiencing from cancer and cancer treatment. And that is NO way to live, NO way to live your life.

"I'll send a referral, but I don't know how quickly they

can get you in."

It took eight days to get into the palliative care practitioner. She was beautiful and lovely, with glowing, loving eyes that understood all the holes in our care that hadn't been addressed for months. She took time to hear about the pain and the nausea, about not being able to eat and sleep, about the pressure in the abdomen, about the worries associated with stage IV cancer. She was smart and quick, with words that came swift and easy, with fingers that flew across the calculator as she tried to determine which patch dose would best alleviate my husband's pain while we continue to navigate this bilirubin issue, while we wait for another CHANCE at treatment. Despite common beliefs, palliative care isn't about dying, it's about trying to LIVE better. It's a CHANCE at living better, a CHANCE to live a higher quality of life than you've been.

I told my husband right there, right then and there in the palliative care room that THIS is the kind of medical work I could do. THIS is the kind of care I'd want to offer people if I was in medicine. In fact, THIS is the ONLY kind of work I'd want to do in medicine. Caring for people and helping people live better. THIS is holy and good work, indeed.

We all have a CHANCE. One CHANCE at life. ONE CHANCE, friends. That's it.

Whether we live well, or whether we live in pain and purposelessness, that's up to us.

Live well every day.

Take a chance now. Now is the only time to do whatever it is you're supposed to do. Now is the only time to do what you WANT to do. Now is the only time to do what you NEED to do. Now is the time.

Live well every single day, even if all feels lost.

This is your moment. This is your time to shine. This is your time to break through and see that you have significance. This is your time to see that your life is a story, and your book isn't finished yet, friend.

Live well every single blessed day, even when

you're exhausted.

Take a CHANCE at sitting and doing absolutely nothing for a moment. Put your feet up. Listen to some cello, stare out at the rain or snow. Wallow in the pain. Be sad. Just cry. Do whatever you need to do to cry. Lament all the things gone wrong. This is your CHANCE.

Live well every joyous day, because this is your LIFE. This is your CHANCE.

Love your parents. Love your kids. Love yourself. Take a look at who you are and be your very best self. Take a look at your parents, your kids, your friends, your loved ones, and every blessed folk you pass by, and say YES, this is our DAY to love and live and take a CHANCE on living our very best life. These people are amazing. I am amazing. I can live and I am here. I am living life. I am alive.

God bless us, we are alive. Today we are alive.

Let us live.

Let us take a CHANCE.

Today.

We live.

44

THE VALENTINE NONE
OF US WANTED

February 27, 2020

We received a call from the oncologist bright and early the morning of February 14, 2020. It was the Valentine none of us wanted, news that Seth's bilirubin had gone up by more than a full point instead of continuing to go down like we needed it to. This news disqualified him from the IDEA196 clinical trial we were supposed to start in Nashville six weeks prior. This news also disqualified him from all trials and treatments for metastatic uveal melanoma available anywhere.

"I'm worried we could be coming close to the end. Our choices are looking pretty limited right now," uttered the doctor with sadness in his voice.

"We're talking about a hospice decision, then," my husband replied.

"I think we are," said the doctor.

We grieved amongst ourselves, shared the news with my husband's parents who had arrived nine days prior to help us out, then called my mom and dad before the kids came home to a hunt for 72-piece boxes of Russel Stover choco-lates Seth had bought weeks ago so they would never for-get this Valentine's Day. We let our two teenagers go on their dates without any worry the bad news would bring. Then we enjoyed pot stickers from a local sushi restaurant, a heart-shaped bake-at-home pizza, and "Chances Are"[1] with my in-laws in the comfort of our living room. It wasn't the romantic end-of-life, last Valentine's Day date you'd imagine with your husband, but it was simply and realistically roman-tic nonetheless.

The next day, we had to tell the kids. Ugh. The conversa-tion NOBODY wants to ever have with kids under 18, all still living at home. Dad's labs went up again. We are out of treat-ment options. Dad is going to be going to heaven to be with Jesus soon. Crying. Crying. More crying. This is so incredi-bly sad, so incredibly painful, something I never, ever want to do again until I am at LEAST 75 years of age, please and thank you, Jesus.

It was then time to share with siblings and our very clos-est of friends. We gave our parents permission to share with aunts, uncles, cousins, and long-time friends who are like family. Within hours, my mom scheduled a one-way flight to Seattle, and my brother-in-law and sister-in-law had sched-uled flights for a four-day visit as well. Four days later, we made the news public – to almost everyone else we've ever known – through a post on Facebook drafted by my husband.

One palliative care appointment and one cancer support group later, I found myself in Whole Foods on the phone with the oncologist, verifying that yes indeed, there are NO trial or treatment options left, that even if my husband's labs mirac-ulously came down into normal range, his body wouldn't be strong enough to withstand the side effects of trials and treat-ments. I asked him twice, just to be sure I heard it right, just to be sure I understood that is exactly what he meant, thanked him for being honest and supportive, and verified that YES, we will be moving forward with hospice.

It's been a whirlwind of 13 days since we received the Valentine none of us wanted.

Thirteen days and we've already met with the hospice intake nurse, head nurse, and head social worker assigned to our case.

Thirteen days and I've already made two emergency calls to the nurse needing recommendations about how to best increase Seth's pain medications.

Thirteen days and I've already spoken at length with Safe Crossings, an organization dedicated to providing pre-bereavement and bereavement services for children.

Thirteen days and the hospice chaplain called.

Thirteen days and we've already had Seth's brother and sister-in-law here for a four-day visit, one set of parents flew out but will undoubtedly be flying back in, another parent flew in, a friend is flying in, and Seth's other brother is flying in for a three-day visit with his girlfriend.

Thirteen days and I have 72 heartfelt texts and a countless number of Facebook messages I probably won't get to for weeks.

Thirteen days and I have lovely folks offering meals even though I haven't even requested any.

Thirteen days and nine playdates from nine different families for our youngest.

Thirteen days and a teen texting big questions about what's going to happen.

Thirteen days and the other teen stepping up to the plate, popping in bedside and couchside to ask how things are going, how are you feeling?

Thirteen days and I wish I could explain how I feel. I wish I could wrap my mind around everything. I wish there was time to process this slower, to experience this more richly, in a timeline that matches the speed of my heart and soul. But life and death don't always follow the perfect pace of our heart and soul, so I'll catch up someday. I'll burst, I just know it. The time will be wrong, but it'll be oh so right. For now, I face each day bravely, as is. Getting pain meds. Getting morning meds. Bringing fresh water with lots of ice. Bringing another chair to our bedroom so we can all watch TV bedside instead of couchside. Sitting on the chair and chatting while Seth tries to eat a little lunch lying down. Sorting through pictures. Taking pictures of pictures. Sending requests for more pictures. Doing finances, canceling credit cards, verifying beneficiaries and bank accounts, making sure all of my licenses are set up and ready to go for plan A and plan B. Meeting with the funeral director. Arranging playdates. Asking for rides. Scheduling the pedicure our teen requested with her daddy. Bothering Seth (again) about finishing his legacy letters for the kids. Tickling him tenderly when he needs it. Taking time to hold his hand and just look at him and feel him next to me. Texting a friend to buy me another four waterproof pillowcases, putting them on top of the waterproof pillowcases I already have on the pillows, then taking them all off again when they're sweaty all the way down to the pillow, then washing them and putting them all back on again once a day, every day, times four pillows. Dealing with daily junk I despise at such a time as this, like phone calls to insurance to get reimbursed for a dealer visit to fix wipers that weren't fixed properly after our windshield was replaced two months ago, and second grade Eureka math that isn't-so-eureka to try and explain and why in the world can't we just put these numbers in columns and add 'em up instead of making this a five-step process? Trying to breathe, fitting in walks or hikes here and there, going to once-a-week grief counseling appointments, attending bi-weekly art therapy support groups, drawing boundaries, knowing what I can and can't do, and working hard to blow it off when I sense other people judging the way the kids and I do life. Remembering that God is still here, even when it's so loud, so busy, way too fast and SO incredibly hard to believe. Believing that I am beloved, that my children are loved, that my husband is loved, even when it feels like we've been assigned to a rare, incredibly abnormal life while the rest of the world gets to go on with normal life. Trusting that God will take care of his son, that we will take good care of our husband, our dad, as we walk him home to heaven. Knowing and resting in every truth. Breathing. Breathing once again.

Hallelujah, this is the Valentine NONE of us wanted. But we will do this. We have done this. We will continue to do this. We will make it through hard things and heavy things and we will all receive healing in due time. Good things will come of this. Good things will come. This is not the end, no. This is not the end. We believe this is not the end.

45

I GOT MY FAIRY TALE

March 24, 2020

My 46-year-old husband was on hospice for 20 days. He was bed bound the final 12 days and confused and disoriented 60-90% of the time in his final eight days. Metastatic uveal melanoma stole his life the evening of March 10, 2020. What started as a single tumor in his eye the first month of 2015 ended the third month of 2020 with countless tumors consuming his liver, abdomen, rib bones, lymph nodes, and spine. At 43 years of age, I am now a widow with three children under 18 years of age.

This is not the fairy tale I imagined my marriage to be.

We were married for 21 years 8 months. I wanted to be the old married couple with heads of gray hair, holding wrinkled hands, taking lazy naps together in the afternoon. I wanted to be the couple that was married 50 years, maybe 60 if we were among the lucky. It was possible. It should've been possible. I wanted to be an example for our children and our grandchildren that love endures all things, believes all things, hopes through all things. I wanted to greet our grandbabies in the hospital, bring our children and grandchildren on a cruise, retire near Florida and visit Walt Disney World as often as we wished, just as we'd planned. I wanted us to die old together. I wanted the great love story.

We planned and assumed all kinds of things for these middle life years. The promotion to Director he'd worked hard for way too long. Family vacations to Colorado, Hawaii, the Mediterranean, Europe, Washington D.C., Australia, Tahiti, Africa, and of course Disney. Homecomings. Proms. Three kids' high school graduations. Three kids' college visits. Three kids' college graduations. Kids' engagements, bridal showers, weddings and daddy/daughter dances, moving kids in and out of dorms, apartments, townhomes, and first homes. Him seeing my dreams to be published come to life. Me seeing his backyard gardens come to life. Us painting the living room, getting curtains, making this house and others our home. Experiencing our prime years together, forever. I wanted all of that for both of us. I planned it would be so.

There were things I wanted to do in the final months and weeks that we never got to do. Take an intimate non-work trip, just the two of us, to a relaxing, warm-weather destination (likely a cruise since that was our favorite). Take the family to Leavenworth, a Bavarian mountain town in Washington for a weekend getaway. A date night to Chihuly Gardens downtown Seattle, a place he'd never been but I thought was beautiful. An intimate dance in our bedroom that he was way too weak for by the time I got up courage to tell him it was one thing I'd still like to do if we could find a way to make it work. I wanted those things for both of us, for all of us. I hoped they would be so.

This is not the fairy tale I imagined my marriage to be.

But as we faced those final days together, it became clear that we DID get our fairy tale. We met and fell in love when we were 18 and 21. Three years later, we were college sweethearts surrounded by 211 loved ones on our wedding day. Not once, but twice, we moved away, far from home, and made a way all our own. We lived in apartments and townhomes and owned three homes together. We made three beautiful children, a boy and two girls. Who could ask for more? I supported his career, and he supported my career, my call to transition careers, and my constant quest to balance family and career. We made beautiful gardens, beautiful homes, and took amazing vacations. We had good friends, good churches, and good neighbors. We loved each other's families and supported each other through thick and thin. We made it to our 20th wedding anniversary PLUS a year and eight months more. And by the end of next month, we would've been together 25 years. The years were getting up there, if I do say so myself.

Times weren't always easy, but that's what makes a good fairy tale. There were years upon years of significant family of origin stressors. He always worked too much. I never found my sweet spot between work and motherhood. He would've preferred I work full-time, always. I knew I couldn't manage full-time work with him working all the time AND be the mom and wife I wanted to be. We experienced a cancer diagnosis, followed by a 9 ½-month layoff, followed by a cross-country move with three kids, followed by a metastatic cancer diagnosis. There were secrets revealed, a problem or two we never truly addressed, and in the last five years of marriage, we discovered the core difference between us that we would've never, ever been able to change. We fought about how much space to put between plants and trees, and it took us forever to agree on pretty much everything we bought for our home. Yeah, we put our two first-born tendencies to the test those 21 years and 8 months!

But every good fairy tale has a resolution, a happy ending of sorts, even if it's sad.

I saw him through health, but I also saw him through sickness. We fulfilled our marriage vows, 'till death do us part. In those final weeks and final days, I was there when one doctor told us it "might be a matter of months," then another told us it might be "weeks," and another agreed it was time to transition to hospice. We did everything, absolutely everything we could do to fight the beast. Everything, I'm telling you. Everything, I'm telling myself. I asked and double asked, checked and double checked, advocated and researched and followed every trail across the nation so my handsome prince could live longer. But it was not to be.

He planned, and I planted trees in his honor. I requested, and he wrote legacy letters to all three children. He bought me a ring to wear with my wedding ring on my right ring finger. We had all the support we needed in those final days, and I had all the alone time I needed with him. We had a beautiful last date in bed, thanks to four beloved friends who made great lengths to make it so. I took opportunities to lie next to him, hold his hand extra long, and kiss him until he couldn't kiss anymore. I said all the things I needed to say. I gave our children every chance to come in and say goodbye to daddy one last time. I heard his beautiful last words to me not once, but twice. Once, the night before he passed, and again the morning he passed. I served him with all my heart those last days. I wasn't a perfect wife, but I was his wife. And when he passed, I was there. It wasn't easy, but I walked him home.

You see, I got my fairy tale.

It just ended sooner than I wanted it to.

A NOTE FROM AMY

Dear Reader,

Thank you for joining me on this journey. It means a lot to know you found value in my words and traded precious time to read them. I trust you have gathered bits and pieces, perhaps even bushels and baskets full of wisdom for the days ahead.

My prayer is that you would live a little differently because of this book. Take care of yourself. Hold loved ones close. Serve like you've never served before. Dare to live greatly and die gracefully. Do everything with the end in mind, but don't wait to do everything until the end. Live with no regrets. And have faith.

Trust that God is guiding you when you can't see what lies ahead. Maybe it's cancer you're facing. Maybe it's divorce or a child addicted to drugs. Maybe it's heart disease, diabetes, or depression. Maybe you lost your home in a tornado. Maybe fires consumed everything you once called yours. I don't know what you're facing today. But I do know this. Your story is important. Your story matters. Your story carries just as much significance as my own.

May God bless you and keep you. May the Lord make His face shine on you and be gracious to you. May the Lord lift His countenance upon you and give you peace.

Live loved, beloved.

Amy

A CONVERSATION
WITH AMY

What are you most glad you did during your cancer season?

From the moment Seth was diagnosed with metastatic uveal melanoma, I did everything I could. Perhaps it was overkill. But I knew in my heart that I needed to come out the other side of cancer feeling confident I did everything I could. That included a whole host of decisions, such as putting a tremendous amount of effort towards becoming brave, being authentic, and securing solid circles of friendship in a new city and state so I had the local support I needed for the journey. I joined every Facebook group I could find for metastatic uveal melanoma so I had access to the inside scoop from real-life patient and caregiver perspectives. Medically, I followed every trail, every path, read research every step of the way. And at the end, I called hospice for extra visits when I knew I wasn't getting enough support. I took advantage of every moment I could by lying next to Seth in bed, holding his hand, calling his parents on FaceTime when I knew we were nearing the end, and bringing our children into our bedroom for final goodbyes on more than one occasion. I advocated fiercely for my husband, myself, and our children.

How did you balance the hope for recovery with the potential for loss?

For the first 3 ½ years, it was fairly easy. I had hope and trust that things were going to work out, that we were going to get through this, that Seth was going to be healed and that he was healed. But once the cancer spread to his liver, it was much more difficult to balance hope for recovery with the potential for loss. I had to be honest with myself about all the possibilities. Being honest with myself about the potential for loss allowed me time to process and live those final two years with no regrets.

Were you able to find joy during this process? Did you have a constant pit in your stomach, or were you able to keep that at bay?

I'll be honest, I had a pit in my stomach more often than not the last two years of the journey. I would describe it more as a constant worry, sometimes dull, sometimes intense, often somewhere in between. I worked incredibly hard to keep my worry at bay, but I am a thinker and analyzer by nature, so it was challenging. The upside was that the worry kept me alert to ALL the things I needed to do, including taking advantage of every moment I had with Seth and every moment we had as a family of five. Certainly, I found joy throughout the journey. But it was the deep joy you can only explain when you're certain God is providing, God is bringing you through even though there's so much uncertainty and so much pain.

Did you change yourself and your true feelings in your relationship because you knew his days were numbered? What did that do to you? For you?

This is a big question and one I don't take lightly. I could write a lot on this and perhaps it's better left for another book, but I'll give it a try. The first 3 ½ years of the journey, I didn't change myself or my true feelings. I trusted we were getting through this and I wasn't numbering our days. But the last two years of the journey when the cancer had spread, I did sometimes keep my truest feelings to myself in an effort to allow Seth to savor life and guard our children's hearts. I carried the burden for our family more than I should have. Perhaps I'll have more healing to do in the future because of it. Then again, I wouldn't change a thing.

What scripture helped sustain you?

The scripture that carried me through was Romans 8:28. "And we know that in all things God works for the good of those who love him, who have been called according to his purpose." I trusted that God was bringing us through this for a purpose greater than I could see and greater than I could imagine. That's the only way I got through it.

Soon after his metastatic uveal melanoma diagnosis, Seth identified 1 Thessalonians 5:16-18 as the scripture that defined him and carried him through cancer. "Rejoice always, pray continually, give thanks in all circumstances; for this is God's will for you in Christ Jesus."

If you could give one single piece of advice to someone in the same shoes, what would it be?

Live with no regrets.

How did cancer impact your marriage? What advice would you give to other couples facing this?

We thought the first 3 ½ years were tough, but it was the last two years that really challenged us as a married couple. Having a rare and serious form of cancer is taxing on a marriage. Our biggest battle was between December 2018 and September 2019 when Seth was on the IMCgp100 clinical trial and we were in this for the long haul, but we also knew the drug wasn't going to work forever. Seth wanted to live a very normal life during that time, while I continued to process the possible reality of losing him at some unknown point down the road. It was difficult to keep my worries to myself and allow Seth to savor life. I'll never forget the "Come to Jesus" moment we had one car ride to Portland when I cried and asked him if he would please just indulge me and honor the reality that I might face life as a widowed mom of three in my future, even if it wasn't imminent. That was a tough conversation for both of us. What advice would I give to other couples facing this? Oh man. God bless you. Do your best. Give yourself grace. Be honest with each other. Listen to each other. Listen well. Compromise where you can. Understand this is going to be difficult, but you will make it. Live well. Die well. Be present for the journey.

How were your parents through all of this and your perception of their pain? Were you able to be helpful to each other?

Our parents were amazing throughout the entire journey. When we were still living in Minnesota, they came to appointments and provided child care whenever we needed it. Once we moved to Seattle, they flew out as often as they could, coordinating and staggering visits so we had the most coverage possible throughout our journey. I also started a Facebook Messenger thread so I could communicate with our moms in written form every step of the way, any time of day.

What were some of the kindest, most loving, sensitive, and caring things someone did for you at each stage in the journey? In other words, can you teach us how to walk beside someone whose life changed in ways they never imagined? Help us be better friends.

I could write a whole book on this. In the meantime, I'll do my best to summarize a few of the most memorable approaches. I will always be grateful for the friend of a friend who provided meals, necessities, and indulgences for us EVERY MONTH throughout our two-year journey through metastatic uveal melanoma. Her faithfulness in serving our family was noteworthy. She didn't know us two years ago, but has become a trusted friend because of her selfless service in our time of need. I'm grateful for a family who sent us cards with words of encouragement, monetary gifts for expenses and special family outings, and gift cards for uniquely identified purposes. These gifts were also sent regularly but randomly throughout the journey. I am grateful for the family who provided several surprise gifts of $500 and $1000, which shocked us, blessed us, and moved Seth to tears every time. And I am grateful for the small but equally important acts of love. A single flower left in a vase by our front door, a package of Mickey ice cream bars dropped off on the way home from the grocery store, a favorite book sent to me in the mail, a gift bag with comfy socks, a journal, and goodies for me before we started the clinical trial. There were so many acts of kindness, I can't even begin to recount. They all mattered, every single one.

What were the words said that were the most comforting? What were the words said to you that brought the most pain?

The words that were most comforting were, "This is not normal." I recounted the details of that encounter earlier in the book. It's a good time to note that "I am so sorry" and "Thinking of you" are safe things to say if you're not sure. To date, the words that have brought me most pain were, "I understand the benefits of your time with a grief counselor, but have you been able to avail to your kids similar counseling?" When you're a young widowed mom, it's painful to have anyone even hint that you're not properly considering or tending the tender hearts of your children. Of course, it was painful to hear the doctor say Seth's cancer had spread to his abdomen and rib bones, and painful again a month later when it spread further to his lymph nodes and spine. It was painful to hear that Seth might have a matter of months, then weeks left to live. And of course, it was painful when the doctor confirmed it was time for hospice.

What part of the journey was most frustrating?

By far, the most frustrating part of the journey was when we were ending the IMCgp100 clinical trial and transitioning to next-best treatment options. I felt confident that liver-directed treatments were the next right thing and I trusted the interventional radiologist, so we went ahead and treated both sides of his liver with Y90 procedures in October and November of 2019. But once those two treatments were complete and we were supposed to move on to another systemic trial, I didn't feel we were given a good option. I had to push hard for a second option, and it wasn't any better than the first option. Ultimately, I had to do my own research, and that's when I found the IDE196 clinical trial in Nashville, which was for Seth's specific kind of cancer and specific gene mutation. Unfortunately, we made two trips to Nashville, but never got to start that trial. Yes, that was the most frustrating and lonely part of the journey.

In the times that you were angry with God, what helped you overcome it?

Good question. I never got too angry with God because I had surrendered to the fact that He was in control, even if I didn't understand why or what He was doing. I got angry with people. Mostly, I got angry with medical professionals and the broken health care system. At my worst, I lashed out at the clinical trial's head nurse for 45 minutes over the phone. I expressed all my anger in regard to what was happening and NOT happening as we were transitioning OFF the clinical trial. I felt alone. I was extremely frustrated. And I didn't feel supported or heard. I expressed the depths of my frustration, vented to friends and family, calmed down as best as I could, got some rest, and began again the next day.

What could our nation and healthcare system do better for families battling terminal or serious health challenges? What would a more compassionate healthcare system look like?

Big questions. HUGE, I tell you. Whether you believe it or not, our healthcare system is BROKEN, filled with holes all over the place. Massive healthcare reform is needed. A more compassionate healthcare system would be patient and family-centered from birth to death. A coordinator would be assigned to rare and serious cases to ensure the patient and family are guided and feel supported throughout the entire process. Healthcare would be set up to address the patient systemically, as a whole person, instead of being treated as a patient who will benefit from a singular medical approach. Nutrition, psychology, social work, physical therapy, occupational therapy, palliative care, and complementary and alternative approaches would be addressed and added from day one and kept in place until the end of care. Expensive? Yes. Necessary? Yes.

How did you navigate the tough medical decisions? Did you just know instinctively what route to take, rely on science, doctors, faith, or all of the above?

I navigated tough medical situations using science, doctors, and faith. The first 3 ½ years of our journey, I trusted doctors and that pretty much worked. But once the cancer metastasized, everything changed. I started that part of the journey believing and trusting doctors blindly, but learned quickly that I was going to need to research and advocate for myself, my husband, and our family. As time went on, I learned who to trust and who not to trust. I learned what to look for in a good doctor, nurse, or health care provider. I learned when to let them lead and when to do my own research. I read a LOT of research. A LOT, I'm telling you. And I stayed highly engaged on the closed Facebook pages with patients and caregivers which helped me stay on top of cutting-edge treatments around the country and globe. Faith played a role as I learned when to trust doctors, when to trust that God might be leading us in a different direction, and when to surrender. No matter what, I had to trust that God was guiding us.

What gave you strength to uncover every rock and search every crevice to keep Seth alive?

I knew at the end of this, I had to feel confident that I did everything I could, that we tried everything. I wanted Seth here for me, for our kids, for our family. I wasn't about to go down without a fight.

Which one of your many skills do you feel was your biggest strength throughout this journey?

I believe my quiet but fierce strength and determination was what first and foremost propelled me through this journey.

Was Seth glad he could work during much of the journey? Were you?

Seth wanted to maintain a "normal life" as long as possible those last two years of the journey. He was a dedicated, loyal employee and thoroughly enjoyed his work. It brought him joy and purpose. He also felt like working kept him well, allowing him to forget about cancer and throw his energies into something productive. He was an all or nothing kind of guy, so I truly believe he needed to stay all in as long as he could. And he did just that, working until January 13, 2020, transitioning to full-time short-term disability on January 14, 2020, less than two months before he passed away. We both felt confident he worked as long as he possibly could, that he worked until he couldn't work anymore. And I feel okay about the way that turned out.

What was the most impactful thing that Seth did for you and your family so he would leave you knowing how much he loved you?

By far the most impactful thing Seth did for me before he passed away was write a legacy letter for each of our children. These letters were near and dear to my heart, as I knew they would be important to the kids as they navigated the rest of life without their dad. Seth ran out of time to write the letter he intended to write for me, but he finished the letters to the kids and that's what matters most. He did write me a beautiful Valentine one month before his passing. That I will treasure always.

How did Seth make you smile during the journey?

Over the course of the last nine months of Seth's life, we had two unusually intimate dates in which we were able to recount our life together and modify our goals as a married couple for the short term rather than the long term we'd always planned. These conversations were priceless, causing me to cry and smile simultaneously. Seth stepped out of his element to dive into those depths with me. For that, my heart smiled in the best way possible.

What moments surprised you in a positive way? And what were some unexpected humorous moments?

Every moment that surprised me in a positive way is related to people's support throughout our cancer journey. I can't even begin to recount all the things people did for us those five years two months. Yes, the biggest, happiest, most joyful surprises were because of people's goodness, generosity, and compassion toward us in our time of need. Most of the unexpected humorous moments came at the very end of Seth's life when he became confused. I told Seth's best friend who flew in the last week before Seth's passing that I hadn't laughed that much in a long time. Some (okay, MANY) of the things

Seth said in his confused state were seriously funny. What else could we do but laugh?

At any point did you pray for peace in your hearts to be the healing instead of physical healing?

I started praying for peace in our hearts when Seth went on hospice. Those prayers escalated dramatically in the final 12 days of his life.

What, if anything, would you have done differently?

If I could go back in time, I probably wouldn't have agreed to the first-line combination treatment of Yervoy and Opdivo. I would have done more research from day one and would have pressed for more information about liver-directed treatment options as a first line of defense since the tumors were confined to Seth's liver at that time. But I didn't know what I didn't know. In regard to regrets of a more personal nature, I don't have any of substance because I worked hard at ensuring I did everything I could along the way. Perhaps there's one thing I regret, which is not revealing early enough that I wanted one last dance with Seth. By the time I believed it was important and got up the guts to tell him, he had little physical stamina left. He got even weaker after that. So yeah. I would have done that differently.

I have another friend who is going through "the year of firsts." In addition to lifting your family up in prayer, how can friends and family best help as this first year moves on with anniversaries, birthdays, and holidays?

I don't have an answer as it's only been five weeks since Seth's passing as I sit here and type. But based on those five weeks of experience which included one holiday, it seems important to mention the deceased's name, talk about them openly, don't be afraid to share a memory or note their absence. It would be lovely to receive an occasional flower delivery with a note that you're thinking of them. Same goes for a nice greeting

card with words of encouragement. Offer a meal or a helping hand if and as it feels right, but don't go overboard. Leave
something special on less-considered holidays such as Father's
Day, Mother's Day, and Valentine's Day. Do everything you
can to tenderly love and care for the individual if they mention their deceased loved one, and if they choose to NOT
talk about their deceased loved one, don't force it. Be gentle and thoughtful in your approach. And whatever you do,
do NOT offer unsolicited advice. Little things go a long way.
Start there.

**Where do you finally settle between "This is God's will for
my family" and "Terrible stuff happens sometimes, and we
just got stuck in the crossfire?"**

I haven't settled on an answer yet and probably won't have
clarity for years. But if I'm a Christian (I am) and claim to
believe the Bible (I do), then faith leads me to trust Romans
8:28 which states, "And we know that in all things God works
for the good of those who love him, who have been called
according to his purpose." I believe I am here, on earth, for
a purpose ordained by God. I believe He works ALL things
together for good. That means He'll work ALL things together
– including really bad things like my husband passing away
from cancer at 46 years of age – for my good so I can fulfill
His purposes here on earth.

**How has cancer changed you? For the worse or better?
How did God show up?**

Cancer has forever changed me. I no longer have the husband I committed to for life. That in itself is life changing.
It's alarming to be a widowed mom of three at 43 years of age,
and I must say it's been a long and hard moment of complete
and utter surrender. I surrender my plans. I surrender my life.
I surrender everything I ever assumed. How did cancer change
me for the worse? Well, I've become much more skeptical of
our healthcare system than I was when our cancer journey

began. And I'm even more sensitive to people being insensitive than I was before cancer, which makes me unforgiving if you cross me wrong. As far as cancer changing me for the better, I'm much better at making friends, and I know how to BE a better friend than I ever have. Seeing my husband die has helped me see more clearly that I am still living; I am still here for a reason. That compels me to risk, be brave, and do hard things like publish this book even though it's nothing like I would've ever imagined my first book to be. Cancer has taught me to love better and live better. And did God show up on this journey? Yes, indeed. He showed up through Seth, our children, through friends and loved ones, but mostly in quiet moments I've yet to reveal. He came in late nights, middle of the nights, and early mornings when stillness set in and competition for my listening ear was scarce. He showed up in words spoken gently, a scripture passage, a simple sentence that helped me know He was there, that He saw me, that He cared, that He was acting and working on our behalf, even when I wasn't so sure anymore and nothing made sense. Yes, he made Himself known in tender ways only I could recognize. That's our God. Guiding us when we can't see a way. He's there. Still. In the stillness, He's there.

ACKNOWLEDGMENTS

My deepest gratitude to all the people who helped along the way.

To Seth, thank you for being my Superman.

To Cooper, Elsa, and Maisie, thank you for the sacrifices you've made because of cancer. We didn't ask cancer to come into our lives, we didn't invite it to stay, and we didn't want it to end this way. Having your dad pass away from cancer is the LAST thing I would have ever wanted for you. I pray you will become stronger, more compassionate, purposeful people because of it. Go forth, living and loving the way your dad would want you to.

To my family and Seth's family, thank you for loving us and supporting us every step of the way.

To the army of friends, neighbors, colleagues, church members, teachers, coaches, and extended family members who came alongside us during our cancer journey, thank you.

To our Cancer Pathways family support groups, Cancer Pathways family grief group, and my Cancer Pathways art therapy group, thank you for being vulnerable and swapping stories so we know we're not alone. Thank you to the gifted social work, mental health, and grief professionals who came alongside us with compassion, including Maddie, Dawn, Geri, Ginny, Karin, Cheryl, Jill, Caitlin, and Camp Sparkle staff. To all the metastatic uveal melanoma patients and caregivers in closed Facebook groups, thank you. You are fierce warriors and advocates.

To all the doctors, nurse practitioners, and nurses from Minnesota, Washington, Oregon, and Tennessee who helped us on this five-year two-month journey through metastatic uveal melanoma, thank you. To Molly, our amazing palliative care practitioner, thank you. To the hospice staff, thank you. We tried everything.

To Taryn Nergaard who completed my book cover design and interior design and formatting, thank you for taking my vision and translating it so beautifully, both on the outside of this book and the inside. I am incredibly pleased. To my editor, Jennie Scott, thank you for helping me master use of the Oxford comma and navigate proper punctuation around quotes. As for citations and the proper use of colons and semi-colons, I'll keep working on them!

To Ginny Owens, thank you for being a beautiful beacon of light in the gap, for becoming a friend, and graciously agreeing to write the foreword at a trying time of your own. You are a gift.

To Anna, Bev, Julie, Katie, Keith, Kris, Maddie, Monica, Peter, Sandra, and Tara, thank you for keeping my secret, reading the manuscript with a two-week turnaround, and agreeing to endorse this book before anyone knew it was going to exist. Your faith is felt.

To the Riverwood writing group, thank you for faithfully gathering all those years, for not calling me crazy when I cried and couldn't see a quick-enough way to my writing dreams, for believing in me as a writer. To fellow writers Bri, Sandra, and Kris, thank you for being gentle with me those first days after diagnosis on the Compassion Sponsor Trip. To the hope*writers who have helped me and supported me on this writing journey, thank you.

To my readers and followers, thank you from the bottom of my heart. Without you, I wouldn't be here. You'll always be the reason I keep writing.

To the people who believed in my writing since the beginning, thank you. You are a small but trusted group. The names Julie, Dan, Judy, Monica, Tom, Lissa, Nicole, Cyndy, Tiffany, Liz, Keith, David, Gina, and Anna come to mind. If I've forgotten you, please forgive me. I see you and I am grateful for you. Your confidence has carried me.

To the Holy Trinity, thank you for making a way, for sending signs of your existence when I need them most, for guiding me when the world looks bleak and dark, for being bigger than any of us can comprehend, and for calling me continually on this road less traveled.

NOTES

Chapter 5: Radiated: Hospital Time Lapse Day One

1. Jennie Allen, Restless: Because You Were Made for More (Nashville: Thomas Nelson, 2013).

Chapter 7: When Beauty Falls

1. Matthew 13:44-46

2. Matthew 14:13-21

3. Matthew 14:22-33

4. Carl Boberg, "How Great Thou Art." (1885).

5. Civilla D. Martin and Charles H. Gabriel, "His Eye is on the Sparrow." (1905).

Chapter 9: Radiated: Hospital Time Lapse Day Five

1. IF:Gathering, www.ifgathering.com

2. Angie Smith, www.angiesmithonline.com

3. Jennie Allen, www.jennieallen.com

Chapter 10: What No Normal Looks Like From Here

1. Kristen Anderson-Lopez and Robert Lopez, "Let it Go." Frozen, performed by Idina Menzel. (Walt Disney Records. 2013).

2. Adele, www.adele.com

Chapter 12: What True Love Is

1. 1 Corinthians 13:4-13

Chapter 14: The Emptying and Filling of a Caregiver's Soul

1. Birdman. Alejandro González Iñárritu. Fox Searchlight Pictures, 2014. Film.

Chapter 20: Like and Unlike Any Other Day

1. Mad Max. George Miller. Warner Bros. Pictures, 2015. Film.

2. Michael Joncas, "On Eagle's Wings." (Oregon Catholic Press, 1979).

Chapter 22: Waiting on Shrinking

1. Amber Haines, Wild in the Hollow: On Chasing Desire & Finding the Broken Way Home (Grand Rapids: Revell, 2015).

Chapter 23: A Tumor, a Piano, Princess, and Waiting

1. Jane Belau, "How Great Thou Art." Concert. 2015, Mayo Clinic.

2. Jane Belau, "The Happy Birthday Song." Concert. 2015, Mayo Clinic.

3. Jane Belau, "The Itsy Bitsy Spider." Concert. 2015, Mayo Clinic.

4. Jane Belau, "The Marine's Hymn." Concert. 2015, Mayo Clinic.

5. Jane Belau, "Somewhere Over the Rainbow." Concert. 2015, Mayo Clinic.

Chapter 32: Cancer is Consuming, But We Are Pressing On

1. Mayo Clinic, www.mayoclinic.org/diseases-conditions/breast-cancer/multimedia/tumor-size/img-20006260

Chapter 33: Celebrating Cancer in the Midst of Christmas

1. José Feliciano, "Feliz Navidad." (RCA, 1970).

2. Johnny Marks, "Holly Jolly Christmas." (Columbia Studios, 1964).

3. Hugh Martin and Ralph Blane, "Have Yourself A Merry Little Christmas." (Leo Feist, Inc., 1944).

Chapter 34: I Did Not Plan Any of This

1. Irving Gordon, "Unforgettable." Performed by Nat King Cole and Natalie Cole. (Elektra, 1991).

Chapter 40: Living Eight Weeks at a Time

1. Father of the Bride. Charles Shyer. Touchstone Pictures, 1991. Film.

Chapter 41: There Aren't Enough Words to Describe Cancer

1. Matthew 27:46

Chapter 44: The Valentine None of Us Wanted

1. Chances Are. Emile Ardolino. Tristar Pictures, 1989. Film.

ABOUT THE AUTHOR

Amy Beth Pederson is a widowed mom of three beautiful children, Cooper, Elsa, and Maisie. She called Minnesota home for most of her life, but now enjoys living in the mountainous suburbs of Seattle. Amy graduated with a master's degree in speech-language pathology from Indiana University. For nearly 15 years, she provided home-based services to families and children with special needs. In late 2014 - just three weeks before her husband's cancer diagnosis - Amy left her career to pursue a longstanding dream of becoming a published author and professional photographer. Amy's deepest desire is to serve women who have experienced serious trials and traumatic life events and help them see the significance of their story. She believes that women need time to process their stories, a safe place to share their stories, and the means to translate those stories into something tangible and lasting. Amy's goal is to pair her gifts of writing and photography with her strong interpersonal skills and life experiences to help women find healing, wholeness, and hope along the way. Amy founded Your Story Studio in 2020 as a means to accomplish these goals and hopes to host retreats someday.

CONNECT

WEBSITE: www.amybethpederson.com

FACEBOOK: www.facebook.com/AmyBethPederson

INSTAGRAM: www.instagram.com/AmyBethPederson

TWITTER: www.twitter.com/AmyBethPederson

Made in the USA
Coppell, TX
24 September 2021